M000032193

HEALTH

BY BIO-ENERGY AND MIND

HEALTH
BY BIO-ENERGY AND MIND

Michael Nudel & Eva Nudel, Ph.D.

BIO-ENERGY SYSTEM SERVICES
Los Angeles, CA

HEALTH BY BIO-ENERGY AND MIND

Copyright © 2000 by Michael Nudel & Eva Nudel, Ph.D.

All rights reserved. No parts of this book may be reproduced or transmitted in any form or by any means, electronic or mechanical, including photocopying, recording, or by an information storage and retrieval system whatsoever without written permission from the publisher, except for brief passages quoted in literary articles or reviews.

Disclaimer: This book is the result of research and experience of the authors, however it is not intended as a medical guide, nor is it to be interpreted or used as a substutute for a professional medical care. Consult your doctor for any serious health problems.
You are responsible for your own health and the health of your relatives. The publisher assumes no responsibility for the efficacy of these techniques, nor do the authors promise any cures. Use caution and common sense, and perform the exercises and techniques gradually.

Published by
Bio-Energy System Services
P.O. Box 461685, Los Angeles, CA 90046, U.S.A.
ISBN 0-9677514-0-3

ATTENTION ORGANIZATIONS, HEALING CENTERS, AND SCHOOLS OF SPIRITUAL DEVELOPMENT:
Quantity discounts are available on bulk purchases of this book for educational or funds raising. Special books or book excerpts can also be created to fit specific needs. For information, please contact Bio-Energy System Services, P.O. Box 461685, Los Angeles, CA 90046 or e-mail, healers@bioenergy-services.com.

Printed and bound in U.S.A.

To my father,
whose death taught
me about life understanding

ACKNOWLEDGEMENTS

We wish to say our heartfelt thanks

To our children, Julia, Meryl, and Kevin, for their unconditional love and acceptance of all we do.
To mother Debora, for her support and understanding of our work.
To brothers, Lev and Vladimir, for their dedication and belief that we do the right thing.
To our friend, Revekka Raynes, who inspired us and made us believe that this project would succeed.

We came from Uzbekistan, Middle Asia. There are three brothers in our family. All of us possess strong inherited bio-energy. My elder brother discovered his ability and began practicing bio-energy healing forty years ago. The time he started using his bio-energy, healing with bio-energy was practiced rarely. Nevertheless, he observed how healers worked and helped people with their energy. My brother had consistently absorbed ancient knowledge of healing because he had felt his unique strong energy flow which could also bring health to others. Since then he has always maintained health of his family. My another brother had also learned methods of bio-energy healing which he always uses in everyday life.

In my childhood I saw dark spots around people, but I did not understand what it meant and turn off this ability until my mid-twenties. When I was seventeen, I felt a necessity of using my bio-energy and asked my elder brother to teach me his methods and techniques. However, that time I was not ready psychologically for serious bio-energetic work.

My first experience of using my bio-energetic ability in an extreme situation was when I served in army in Kazakhstan, then former republic of Soviet Union. We were cutting reeds when one soldier cut his hand with coarse reed stem. Blood started to flow as fountain from his hand. I was near and sent as much powerful flow of my energy as I can through my hands without delay. I continued sending my energy and saw the blood flow was started to thicken and stopped entirely in three minutes.

I remember one more situation in Kazahkstan when I used my bio-energy to help people. There was not any medical center for tens of miles around, and people had lived in desert without medical help. I offered my help when I saw a crying child with high fever in one household. I approached my hands to that child trying to recognize the root of the prob lem and perceived that it was her stomach. I began working with my bio-energy over the child. The child stopped crying, calmed down and fell asleep very soon.

Since then I have applied my bio-energetic ability to help people for thousands times in my life. Later I could bring high blood pressure or fever down over the phone and perform healing in face and at any long distance as well. I have always tried to develop traditional methods of energy healing and systemize my knowledge and experience of bio-energy healing. I have always wanted to make it accessible for everyone who interested in the learning because everybody possesses with bio-energy less or more. I consider my system of healing one of the most attainable, clear and effective systems of bio-energy healing which exist today. My system of healing has proved with many successful outcomes for twenty-five years.

Once I met a famous healer in Uzbekistan. The woman was about a hundred years old. I told her that I chose another career than healing people with my energy, but something from within "was pushing" me to use my energy to help people. She looked at my hands and told me that two stars on my palms predict a healer's strength inside of me which in turn determines my healer's consciousness. Moreover, she mentioned that a cut on a specific part of my palm showes a possibility of marriage to a woman with a weak liver.

I had never asked my future wife about her liver conditions and I almost forgot about the prediction until my wife suddenly got a serious liver disease a few years after we were married. In 1986 doctors discovered liver abscess in my wife and told me that my wife was in a critical condition. She was put in a special intensive care room. Doctors performed operation and did everything possible to save her life. Although doctors did their best, they said that my wife would pass away in a few days. After talking with doctors in a hospital, I decided to assist doctors to save my wife.

Stopped my emotions and precisely concentrated, I began performing healing with my methods to my ailing wife. My wish to help my loving wife was so great and my energy was so powerful that I won.

Thereafter, surprised doctors predicted a full disability for the rest of my wife's life because four more people with the same diagnosis got disability and one patient died at that time. Nevertheless, my wife returned to her work after hospital in a perfect physical condition.

One more forthcoming sad experience had been awaited us. In 1988, my wife was infected with Hepatitis B while receiving shut. Her condition was critical again and the liver became weakened greatly. Applying my methods of healing, I helped my wife to recover quickly and return to normal life. With my bio-energy, I effectively restored my wife's health so we could have two more children born after. And now my wife remains in a perfect health helping me in my endeavors.

I consider bio-energy one of the miracles of a great power given us by God, and that everybody can develop energetic ability and perform bio-energy healing in order to help self and other people.

Table of Contents

Illustrations

HOW TO CONTACT THE AUTHORS

Michael Nudel and Eva Nudel, Ph.D. provide distant energy healing and bio-energy system assessment and services for individuals, organizations, and businesses. Requests for information and services should be directed to them at the address below. Readers of this book are also invited to contact the authors with comments and ideas for future editions.

Michael Nudel and Eva Nudel, Ph.D.
Bio-Energy System Services
P.O. Box 461685,
Los Angeles, CA 90046

Web site: http://www.bioenergy-services.com
E-mail: healers@bioenergy-services.com

Introduction

This book presented detailed information concerning how you can develop phenomenal abilities to heal yourself, your family, friends and even pets with bio-energy: your energy with help of your hands and mind. The art to heal people by hands' energy dates back to ancient times. Jesus Christ performed healing by hands' energy, and many other ancient healers directed their energy into healing process. There is an erroneous belief that healing using bio-energy is possible only for people with extraordinary abilities. This assumption has been proven to be false, because everyone possesses innate capabilities and, with proper training, he or she can develop them.

Methods and exercises in this book will show how you can develop a powerful memory, positive thinking, improve your sense of inner-self and your outer energy's field of awareness. In this book we give you a new theory about the ability to receive, accumulate and transmit vital energy from the cosmos, and how to protect yourself from negative energetic information. You will be able to feel your own flow of bio-energy, and that of others, and how to control it. In addition, you will learn how to assess energy states of other people, how to heal yourself and your relatives through the use of bio-energy accumulated in your own organism, and how to perform absentee healing as well. The techniques in this book teach you to know how to use bio-energetic method in everyday life, and you will learn how to develop the use of subtle energetic bodies that surround you.

Healers must be in absolute perfect health. Besides physical health, it is also important to maintain psychic and energetic health to live in harmony with nature. Physical, psychic and energetic health are mutually related because they cooperate with each other. Moreover, mind rules physical, psychic and bio-energy of a human being; therefore it is necessary to learn how to develop mental control over each state in order to achieve mastery of the healing process.

People need medicine to intervene when acute illnesses, accidents, and other emergencies occur. On other hand, people automatically try their best to prevent chronic illnesses that result from stress, aging, or inactivity. Wise people have learned to fight, or prevent any illnesses with drugless bio-energetic therapy.

This book allows you to discover the opportunity to heal yourself and others with bio-energy, and teaches you how to develop this ability and perform it practically. You will learn to maintain your health on a positive energetic level around your body, receive energy from the cosmos. You can begin to maintain your own energy level, and also load your body with cosmic energy. You will learn to feel your bio-energy field and that of others. You will discover that, on the energetic level, an illness is expressed in the alteration of the density of the biological energy field when it occurs in weak organs of the body. Eventually you will be able to open hidden abilities of people, maintain their health on the energetic level, and heal illnesses and even prevent sicknesses.

You will learn to breathe correctly, and reduce stress and achieve effective relaxation. We show you techniques of relaxation, mental concentration, and proper breathing. In other words, healing by energy requires the healer to breathe correctly, gather more energy by breathing exercises, and develop a strong bio-energy field with high levels of energy in specific energetic centers. The exercises develop and maintain a strong memory, and the yoga exercises sustain inner endurance of the organism.

By studying Hatha-Yoga and Pranayama exercises and poses, you will learn how to breathe properly, meditate, center yourself, relax, gain a life energy, massage your internal organs, keep the body healthy and flexible, and accelerate removal of toxins from the organism. Hatha-Yoga teaches how to concentrate attention precisely, and the skills necessary for development before practicing the art of healing with bio-energy.

Every individual wants to be healthy in order to live longer life and enjoy being on Earth. However, maintenance of great health takes practice. By starting early, you can preserve your life and others by avoiding illness. In our book, we describe ancient teaching techniques for understanding different methods and opportunities to learn how to maintain health, and to develop positive character traits.

Our organisms possess amazing abilities to heal themselves. But the conditions of the environment in which we live (fast food, alcohol abuse, drug dependencies, polluted air, chemicals, toxins, high-tech stress,and loss of bare foot connections with soil), harms our bodies. A lack of knowledge about how to keep our bodies, souls and minds functioning properly prevents development of physical, psychic, and energetic strength, and makes us susceptible to all sorts of illnesses, stresses, depressions, addictions and negative states of mind.

Bio-energy will help us maintain health and manage our environment "energetically" in everyday life. This book presented step by step and how-to-do information to develop bio-energetic ability and healer's attitude to help selves and others.

Chapter One

Human Energetic Bodies

Every epoch brings its own knowledge and understanding. For a long time in Western history, it was accepted that the mechanistic model of the Universe was. The mind was separated from the mind and body. Westerners equated their identity with the mind, instead of with their whole organism. This fragmentation led to perceiving the world from "outside," or viewing it as a multitude of separate objects and events. The view alienated us from nature and our fellow human beings.

There was a period in history when materialists and idealists argued about the priority of Being. Materialists claimed that the material was a primary reason for existence. On the other hand, idealists believed, that the consciousness was primary, and energetists argued that energy was the origin. Nevertheless, modern atomic physics united all three theories into one. Moreover, physicists discovered that matter is not matter, as people have considered it for many centuries, but energy. They also accepted that everything in the Universe depended on our consciousness, and attention to events and occurrences.

Understanding self is the beginning of understanding the World, and Laws that control it. Physicists proved the Eastern understandings of the world were valid, and mystics emphasized the basic unity of the universe, and interrelation of all things. The Eastern views maintain that the awareness of interconnectedness, dynamic motion, and continual change of all things and events in the cosmos are inseparable from reality which is alive, spiritual, and material at the same time.

The modern model of the Universe accepts the concept of the unity of the microcosm (a human), and the macrocosm (the Universe). However, individuals live in the biosphere of this planet.

Everything in the universe consists of energy. Everything is interconnected. All our thoughts and mental states are energy. As parts of a cosmic organism, we are energy beings.

The most amazing fact is that we have electromagnetic fields around us. These energy fields are nonmaterial, and they are associated with human emotions or thoughts as forms of energy. Any live organism has a special structure - a biological field. The bio-energy field of a human consists of subtle bodies with their energetic potentials, and which give strength and power to the biological field. Energetic potential depends on the conditions of physical and psychic health, and, perhaps, astrological factors. For example, experienced psychics can feel human energy fields with their hands with out touching a body, and, sometimes, even see a glowing aura around individuals.

Many views and hypotheses about bio-energy exist nowadays, and some many researchers call it psi-energy. Special experiments in the laboratories enabled researchers to discover waves of energy emitted by humans. With mental activities the waves changed with speed of thought: the thought was followed by energy. Electric charges in the human's head change on different levels of consciousness. The electric field of a human is the unity of positive (+) and negative (-) electric zones. In order to be healthy, the energetic balance must be maintained in the bio-energy system. Energetic balance and constant freely flowing of energy are important factors in your health and well-being.

Worlds of the Universe

Modern cosmology views our Universe consisted of a few worlds, which have their own characteristics, own energy, material, and time. Acquired with informative field of the earth help, knowledge and insight of researchers in theory of space and time allow us to consider the Universe as multidimensional. We live in three-dimensional space (height, width, and length), and time expresses any biological movement. Nevertheless, in our real world there are other personality characteristics, such as: strong will, intellect, intuition, and love, which make up complex worlds (coordinates of four-, five-, six-, seven-dimensional space).

Ancient philosophies enlightened Absolute (or Akasha) as a subtle substance of the Universe. The Absolute World had an infinite number of dimensions. And past, present, and future are dissolved in the Absolute world. White is the color of the Absolute, which symbolizes circuit of creation and love.

White is universal color. Light is white or invisible, and universal energy vibrations are white or invisible as well. When an artist blends all colors of rainbow, he creates a united summary color white. White is summary of all colors of the visible spectrum - the universe's electromagnetic scale. The visible spectrum manifests in light that we can see. The colors are contained in white light. Moreover, colors are waves of different vibratory rate. The waves of seven rainbow colors vary in length, which is the distance from the crest of one wave through its through to the crest of the following wave. And each color has its own unique wavelength. Moreover, every world of the Universe has its own color or its energy corresponds to fluctuating waves of their specific color.

As white light contain seven different colors, our Universe unites seven primary worlds, as follows:

1. Three-dimensional world, which material and energy corresponding to the fluctuating waves of red.

2. **Ether** world. This energetic world does not contain living organisms, but their energetic matrixes. Its energy corresponds to fluctuating waves of orange. Its energy goes to movements of living organisms of the Earth.

3. **Astral** world consists of the gravitational field of the Moon. Energy and material correspond to fluctuating waves of yellow.

4. **Mental** world (four-dimensional space) consists of the gravitational field of the planets of the Solar system. Energy and material correspond to fluctuating waves of green.

5. **Karmic** world (five-dimensional space) consists of the gravitational field of the Sun. Material and energy

correspond to fluctuating waves of blue.

6. **Intuitive** world (six-dimensional space) consists of the gravitational field of our Galaxy. Material and energy correspond to fluctuating waves of dark blue.

7. **Nirvana** (seven-dimensional space or "World of Love") consists of the gravitational field of the Universe. Material and energy correspond to fluctuating waves of violet.

The five, additional intermediate worlds are red-orange, light-orange, mental-karmic (turquoise), intuitive-karmic (sky blue), and supermental (turquoise-purple). They play a special role in achievement of harmony in the cosmic development through their developments or perfect combinations.

Human Bodies of Energy

Humans are children of the cosmos. All our organs correspond to energies fluctuating in the cosmos. According ancient teachings subtle worlds of the cosmos create our individual bodies. Like the Universe, our energetic system consists of seven worlds, and has seven primary bodies (or auric layers) that interact with each other. These bodies consist of the material and energy of the corresponding universal worlds accordingly, deal with them, and receive the energetic information from them. Besides the physical bodies, our individual energy system consist of ether, astral, mental, karmic, intuitive, nirvana, and absolute subtle energetic bodies, which form our aura - human energy field. We call energetic bodies subtle because it is difficult to perceive them with our senses. Nevertheless, we can perceive them when specially trained and used bio-energy methods and techniques.

All subtle bodies in a human energy system communicate with each other, and with the physical body, through the energetic "transformers"- chakras. Chakras transform cosmic universal life-support energies into human energy systems. In Sanskrit, the chakra is a wheel of life. Indian tradition considers invisible chakras as centers of consciousness. All humans have chakras whether we aware of them or not. Chakras are, in fact, centers of different levels of consciousness, ranging from almost bodily to highly spiritual.

Healthy chakras spin all the time bringing energy to the physical body and all its energy layers. Chakras play a very important role in well-being and health. Chakras are an important part of bioenergy systems. The locations and functions of the major chakras are closely related to the endocrine system and autonomic nervous system. The chakras are located on the spinal column, the head, and one chakra is located in the heart plexus (see Figure 1).

The first chakra is **Muladhara** (the root chakra). It is located in the coccyx. The color is red. This chakra represents the physical body and corresponds to it.

The second chakra is **Svadhisthana** (the sacral chakra), and it is located in the sacrum (lower abdomen). The color is orange. The chakra represents ether energetic body (energetic matrix of the physical body) and corresponds to it.

The third chakra, **Manipura** (the solar plexis chakra), is located on the fifth lumbar (abdomen) vertebra. The color is yellow. It relates to the astral body. It depends on emotional condition of the person and can change its form due to personal conditions.

The fourth chakra is **Anahata** (the heart chakra). It is located on the 5th thoracic vertebra (chest). The color is green. It relates to the mental body (mind, related to intellect).

The fifth chakra is **Vishuddha** (the throat chakra). It is located on the first thoracic vertebra, on the thyroid level (throat). The color is blue. It connects to the karmic body (ego).

The sixth chakra is **Ajna** (the third eye). It is located on the second cervical vertebra(the forehead). The color is dark blue. It is connected to the intuitive body ("superconsciousness", intuition). Ajna chakra is a center of physical energy.

The chakra of Nirvana is Central chakra. It is located on the heart plexus. The color is violet. This is the link between our physical body and Nirvana ("World of Love").

The seventh chakra is **Sahasrara** (the Crown Chakra).
It is located on the top of the head. The color is white. It is linked to Absolute body (the conclusion of the development of all seven bod ies of a cosmic organism). Sahasrara chakra is a center of psychic energy, and the only chakra that follows its subtle body Absolute

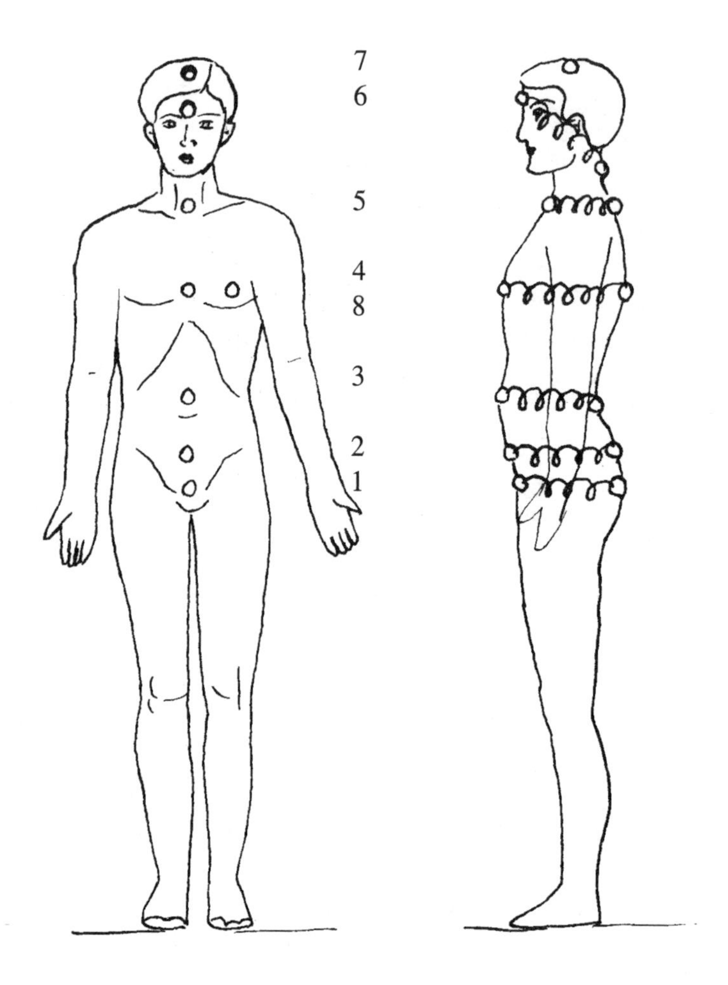

Figure 1. Chakras

1. Muladhara
2. Svadhisthana
3. Manipura
4. Anahata
5. Vishuddha
6. Ajna
7. Sahasrara
8. Central

in cosmic spheres after death. It is the center of psychic energy of the human organism. Through Sahasrara chakra, we connect to the "Divine Center".

Human bodies of energy are complex structures as compared to the physical body. The **ether body** lasts up to two inches over our physical body. During prenatal development, the solid body of a fetus is constructed according to the matrix of ether body, and it is its exact duplicate. During its life cycle, ether body performs a function of a constructor, which builds and restores the solid body. Healthy ether body differs by an accumulation of energy, which goes through the solid body and influences its organs positively.

Many researchers believe that the chakra of the physical plan - Muladhara - and Svadhisthana belongs to the ether body. Certainly they are similar to each other by their energetic functions as well. Muladhara plays a connecting role between the center of the physical energy (Ajna-chakra) and the center of the psychic energy. Muladhara-chakra absorbs important for physical body elecromagnetic fields of the Earth. Svadhisthana, which produces internal energy, feeds by prana or vital energy of the food matter, which it distributes to the organs of the physical body and other energetic centers along energy pathways. Interactions of Svadhisthana with other chakras determine the influence of food intake on energetic manifestations (Manipura-chakra), sexuality (Muladhara-chakra), and emotional spheres (Anahata-chakra).

The **astral body** possesses extraordinary mobility and, depending on emotional state, can accept different shapes and sizes. Movement in astral bodies in areas of activity of the gravitational field of the Moon is possible if done under supervision of experienced professional. The primary chakra of the astral body is Manipura-chakra. This center accumulates and distributes energies which are produced in other chakras. Through Manipura, energy and material of the astral world are united.

The **mental body** (mind, intellect) connects to our physical body by meridians (energy pathways). It is the strongest body among others. If intellect is high in its development, then the mental body is developed perfectly. We use the mental bodies in our actions, behaviors, and thoughts.

Karmic body is a ruler of our ego. All events, their reasons, and all of the unconscious traits of past lives that determine individual's being and destiny, are kept in the karmic body (karma). Karmic body rules all functions of a cosmic organism. It connects to the karmic world by the Vishuddha chakra.

Intuitive body contacts to the intuitive world by Ajna-chakra (the third eye), which can be a source of intuitive insight and superconsciousness (unconscious sphere of consciousness). Intuitive body develops more or less in all people. Many people have experienced moments when their intuition yelded the most intelligent decision at unexpected times. Besides controlling vision of the past, the intuitive body directs the future.

The chakra of Nirvana body -Central chakra- is a connection between a physical body and Nirvana body through the heart. A peak of our soul is a body of Nirvana, which acts as fusion of our ego and the Universe, and union of Truth and Love.

And the last body - **Absolute body** - is a consequence of the development of all bodies of a cosmic organism. If a human life is improved due to karma, so the Sahasrara-chakra regulates human behavior in according to changed expectations of life.

Aura

Aura is any invisible "radiance" around matter. All things and humans possess their own special aura. There is no dead material, everything in nature lives, breathes, moves in energy flux. Any planet in the Universe radiates its own color as any living organism's aura or chakra does. Humans possess the most complicated and powerful aura. From the beginning of life, human bodies are wrapped "invisible" coverings, which may be perceived by psychics as glowing, differently colored, or cloudy.

Those people who are clairvoyant may perceive these beautiful "colored" energies, and see others. Each person has special nuances of auras, because the whole aura may be seen as a result of the development of energetic bodies. The greater our spiritual growth, the brighter and larger the aura. Elderly people have gray, discolored aura. Clairvoyants may see dark gray or black spots on a human aura, which means there are energetic imbalances in the bio-energetic system and physical illnesses. When one dies, aura disappears. Aura cannot be seen around dead people.

Even ordinary people may see aura after being in a dark room for a few hours. Many healers offer instructions about how to start seeing aura of ordinary people. They suggest gazing on a white wall through one's head will let them see white clouds glowing around the head. To see aura is not so important as to feel it. In this book we offer the complete program how to feel and heal the aura.

Aura, which is given to us from the birth, is in constant energetic flux of change. The most amazing thing is that it may be consciously developed during a lifespan. A great developed and highly spiritual aura gives health and long life to our physical bodies.

Development of Energetic Bodies

A very developed ether (orange) body makes an individual hardy and able to work well and hard, and excludes illnesses. All energetic bodies acquire energy from the ether body; especially the astral body which needs it. With the development of the ether body, the astral and intermediate bodies grow as well. Examples of high development of the ether body are great physical health, hardiness, high capability to work hard, flexibility, physical strength, and powerful potential.

Recommendations for the development are breathing exercises, hatha-yoga, sport, proper nutrition, regular detoxification, and exercises helping to restore bio-energy (we will learn about it later).

The important figures of the astral body (yellow) are vivacity, activity, vitality, cheerfulness, ability to feel joy, and laughter. High degrees of the development of the astral body occur due to the ability of deeply developed identification with the image of other individuals besides self. We can consider a daily cold shower (water is filled with astral energies), walking barefoot on the ground, meditation using and imagining the tastes, smells, warmness or coldness, as special exercises for the development of the astral body.

Examples of high development of mental body (green) are creativity, quantity and total volume of knowledge, logic, memory, velocity of the thought process, eagerness to acquire philosophic and scientific knowledge, absence of emotions in the thought process, and self-control. In the process of the accumulation of the knowledge and development of intellect, factors like superiority, haughty mind, and overexciting can be restraining.

The karmic world is more subtle and dynamic than the mental world. Many teachings about psychic development mention that the karmic body (blue) plays an important and cardinal role among other bodies. Strength of the karmic body connects to the knowledge of an individual and fulfillment of the primary Law of karmic development, or all terms and laws of structures in which we act. Perfect development on the karmic plan breaks addictions or bad habits permanently. It also controls our thoughts and emotions. It helps to maintain psychic health and to develop all colors. Examples of high development of the karmic body are perfect attention, economy and rational use of the strengths, means, energy, time, fulfillment of duty, concentration, unselfishness, and realization and observance of norms in human behavior.

Development of the intuitive body (dark blue) is related with development of intuition (power in feeling of harmony or disharmony in any object, meaning, or event).

Primary examples of high development of intuitive body are tendency to harmony, beauty, intuitive feeling of consonance and dissonance, knowledge of harmony laws of the world around self, ability to visualize images, perfect sight and hearing, memory, practicing to enter into dreams, and development of spirit sight (the third eye). One of the most effective techniques of development of a third eye is visualization. At first you may try to visualize a specific color and hear a corresponding sound in state of relaxation. Next try to see and hear combinations of colors and sounds, and imagined geometric figures (you will learn this later). When the third eye is developed perfectly, seeing or feeling energetic fields around living people becomes possible.

If you would like your Nirvana body (violet) to grow, you have to recognize your "enemies" (ego, or love to self), and negative traits like fear, envy, hatred, jealousy, distrust, and lies. Factors of the development of Nirvana are spirit cleanliness, trust, kindness, compassion, ability to live for others, and truth. Meditations are about relaxation, dissipating ego, concentration on the heart, and developing necessary traits to help to grow into Nirvana body.

Harmonic unity of all best qualities, all kinds of development is the Absolute body. Full development of all bodies gives the energy to the Absolute body - Kundalini-Shakti possibility to flow through all chakras to Sahasrara-chakra and let an individual perceive the information from Absolute.

It is necessary to mention that the balance of the development all bodies is not necessarily desired, because equilibrium blocks growth. The interchange of energy from inside and outside remains virtually constant, and it prevents fluctuations to the next level of development. Thereafter, changing of rhythms, which can be done by conscious violation of the state of equilibrium, or choice of one or two types of the development at a time can help to create a great personality.

The intermediate bodies, such as mental-karmic, intuitive-karmic, and supermental, play important roles in the development of a cosmic organism. Mental-karmic development demands unity of mind and will, control over mind, possibility of thoughtful decision, systemization of knowledge, philosophical teachings, clarity of thought, and dismissing unnecessary thoughts and images. Intuitive-karmic development differs from mental-karmic in placing goals before selves and finding ways to achieve them by using intuition in the choice of goals. The primary qualities of intuitive-karmic development are unity in karmic qualities and harmony, systemization of the knowledge of art, and use of it for meditation and growth of psychic strength. And, development of supermental body is harmonic combination of mind, will, and love.

Chapter Two

Your Bio-Energy Level and Ability to Heal

There is an undiscovered ability of bio-energy flowing through your hands. Your hands may be "energetic" too, and you may make everyday use of it. Aside development of your subtle energetic bodies and creation your personality, you can develop an ability to feel energy fields with your hands. You can also develop ability to "regulate" and modulate energy fields around you or other people with your hands, thus influence your physical and subtle bodies with healing energy relieving imbalances in energy fields and bringing health and energetic balance.

Bio-energy can be explained as bio-electromagnetic energy. You can hear about terms of positive and negative energy in bio-energy healing. We will use the term of bio-positive energy meaning pure healing energy coming from God. Positive energy flows freely in energy systems bringing vitality and health. Whereas definition of bio-negative energy is trapped, disharmonious, stale, or stagnant energy that blocking pathways and prevent vital energy from freely flowing in energy systems. Negative energy brings imbalances into energetic systems, and it is connected to illnesses and emotional trauma.

Human energy fields of different people may interact with each other also bringing energetic imbalance or discomfort, but you will be able to fix any imbalance energetically. The vital energy can be transferred from person to person. With instructions in this book, you will be able to perform bio-energy healing or energetic management. Even if you do not choose to become an energy healer after reading our book, you will still be able to control any condition, event, or situation in your life energetically. If you choose to help yourself, your loved ones and your pets with the life-supporting energy in your hands, you will maintain an energetic balance in their energy fields which bring them health and vitality.

The idea of human energy transfer for healing is not new. People performed healing by human energy for thousands of years. The knowledge of the energetic method of healing came from ancient India to Egypt, Greece, China, Israel and other countries. Jesus Christ used laying-on of hands as a method of healing.

Some healers name the method "ethereal healing," and consider it healing of the ether body, and some healers consider it as pranic healing because a vital energy is Prana. We think bio-energy of healer's hands to bring healing and benefits to all human energy bodies as the whole energy system. Nevertheless, in this book you will learn unique techniques and exercises, which will allow you to possess the bio-energy healing method and special techniques in order to maintain health and widely use it in everyday life for all purposes.

Sensitive people with healthy energetic systems can feel biological fields of others. They "activate" hands energetically, bring their hands close to the body surface at a certain distance, examine the field, and feel all characteristics of a person's energetic field. They may experience heat, cold, some density, pressure, shock, tingling, or pulsation. To recognize an illness or an energetic imbalance of a healee, healers use their knowledge of all these sensational feelings, strong memory and their mastery of the art. And, by their bio-energy and mind, healers can "fix" energetic imbalances or free stagnant energy from the healee's energy field.

Thereafter, they can prevent an illness on the physical level, comfort ill persons, eliminate pain, accelerate the physical body's healing, heal an illness, improve a physical condition, and maintain a positive emotional and mental state of a healee.

The most interesting fact is that everybody can perform healing by energy, not just people with extrasensory perceptions (ESP). We developed and systemized classical forms of energy transfer and hands-on healing and, moreover, created our own bio-energy method which may be used as a method of energetic man agement in everyday life. We state that human health is a summary of physical, psychic (mental), and energetic conditions of person. And people have to live in energetic unity with all things around. We would like to offer you valuable information about how to develop an ability of energetic healing and manage yourself, your relatives, pets, and your environment on the energetic level.

Healing by energy requires from healers the development of abilities to control their own energy consciously, calm the mind at will, breathe correctly, gather energy by breathing exercises, have a strong bio-energy field, high level of energy in energetic centers (chakras), have strong and capacious memory, visualize, feel and estimate work of own body, listen to the inner-self, estimate own feeling, and be practically healthy. People become energy healers when they change the consciousness, a world view, and mental and physical attitude of themselves.

At first you can determine the level of your bio-energy. For beginners, we suggest that you check the strength of your field with the following exercise:

Cut a thin stripe from cigarette paper. And hang it on nylon or silk thread on the shoulder level. Keep your hands extended at the distance 2 feet to the paper, and begin to make movements by your right hand as you play a ball moving it forth and back of the hanged paper. If the paper starts moving, you have bio-energy strength. Start to do the same procedure with your left hand, and with both hands. Stepping back, do the same procedure from further distance changing the distance until the paper does not move. If you could do it from the distance of 6 feet, you have a strong bio-energy field. If not, you can still increase your energetic potential and develop energetic abilities reading our book.

The following chapters you will learn how to develop energetic potential of your bio-field, and how it can be increased in a combination: physical, psychic, and energetic health.

We possess incredible strength - our bio-energy. If you employ it consciously, it will give you tremendous power, and ability to heal yourself and others from physical, spiritual and mental problems. Step by step we will show you that it is possible to control energy consciously. Moreover, you will be able to perform "distant mental healing" and "healing on a photograph". Yes, it is possible.

Everyone possesses a more or less powerful bio-energy field which interacts with fields of others. You will learn about how to manage life situations with your bio-energy. With power of your own bio-energetic field, and energy in your hands, you can become a healer. Even if you use this knowledge for yourself and your loved ones, you will see how your life will be happier, energetic, and fulfilling.

Energy on the Physical Level

On the physical level people receive energy from food, and through rest and sleep. Every activity demands energy. Besides physical processes in the body, emotions, thoughts, and overreactions to the outside world depend on energy. Stress, anxiety, grief, and unhappiness consume plenty of energy. Excess of emotions, work, sex, eating, and alcohol drinking can leave people enervated. Sometimes people feel a lack of energy even when they ate and rested well.

The ability of the organism to heal itself depends on energy, too. The body cannot heal itself when it is out or low in energy. Disease is an energetic imbalance in the organism. People with strong immune systems can resist to illnesses easily and when they have energy enough to fight disease. On the other hand, disease can occur in deprived of energy physical body. Maintaining health, people need to control energy level in the bodies as well. When people spend energy greater than the energy accumulated, they have lower level of energy in their physical bodies. When people feel their her bodies enervated, they begin feel worse. Moreover, enervating brings weakening to organisms. If people have generically weakened zones in the bodies, these zones become attacked first by illnesses or toxins.

Energy levels depend on a life-style. When people want to be energetic, they may choose healthier life-style with minimum things which can enervate them. By review events of a day, people can evaluate their communication with others, behavior in different occurrences, reaction on circumstances and surroundings around them to determine how events can deprive them of energy, and what they can change to avoid energy deprivation. If people work hard, they can spend leisure time on eating wholesome food, dreaming, total rest, walking on the fresh air, taking a bath, and get early sleep to accumulate energy for the next day of work. Saving energy is not refusing of active life style, exercising, or activities, but spend ing priceless energy right, and not more than it can be accumulated.

Bio-Energy Accumulation

Healing with bio-energy requires spending some bio-energy at act of healing. As open energetic system, you may receive our energy from the cosmos, not only with food or sleep. You will especially need to receive extra energy from cosmos, if you perform bio-energetic work. You may refill your bio-energy receiving it from cosmos, and accumulate it in an energetic reservoir - your bio-energy field.

Now we will talk about receiving energy from the cosmos (universe). When reached a higher level of consciousness, prepared selves spiritually and mentally, healers may learn how to receive energy from the cosmos.

Vital cosmic energy is called **Prana** in Sanskrit, and it acts in the transfer of human energy. Prana is breath of life. Healthy people have this energy in abundance. Freely flowing Prana in the human energy systems brings vitality and vivacity into organisms. However, ill people have deficits in this energy. They have gray constricted energy fields with blocked and stagnant energy. Such a condition of the energy fields affects people's health, bringing energetic imbalances and illnesses on the physical level. Old people have deficits of prana.

We cannot see prana, only its manifestations. This vital energy penetrates everywhere coming from Great Unknown. Prana submits to human consciousness, and can be creative as well as destructive. Once you learn how to accumulate this energy, manipulate it, control, and transfer it, you will become an energy healer or bio-energy master. You will enjoy using creative prana for all purposes in your life.

When you discovered that your level of bio-energy is not enough for healing performance or for everyday tasks, it demands the following exercises. They are very important to perform after every act of healing to restore your bio-energy level. The exercises help to increase bio-energy of the organism, and to turn on internal reserves of your organism.

1. Increasing the bio-energy level.

Stand or sit, and raise your hands with palms inward (Figure 2), and center on the inner self. Make the inhalation, and imagine that billions of cosmic energy particles enter your fingertips, and open bio-energetic active points on them. You will feel a light tin gling, a little electricity, or goose bumps.

On the exhalation: send this energy inside the hands to fill the wrists.

On the inhalation: send more energy to the fingertips.

On the exhalation: send the energy inside the body to fill the arms.

On the inhalation: send more energy to the energetic "gates" on the fingertips.

On the exhalation: energy goes inside filling palms, arms, and forearms.

On the inhalation: receive more energy at the fingertips.

On the exhalation: energy goes inside the body following hands, shoulders, and neck.

On the inhalation: send more energy to the fingertips opening bio-energetic points.

On the exhalation: energy goes inside, filling hands, shoulders, neck, and face (from down to up). Here you can use this self-suggestion: "My face rids itself of wrinkles, becomes youthful, and begins to sparkle with delightful color."

On the expiration: send more intensive flow of the energy to the fingertips.

On the exhalation: energy goes inside filling hands, shoulders, neck, face, Ajna - chakra (third eye), and forehead.

On the inhalation: intensive flow of the energy flows to the fingertips.

On the exhalation: energy goes through hands, shoulders, neck, face,

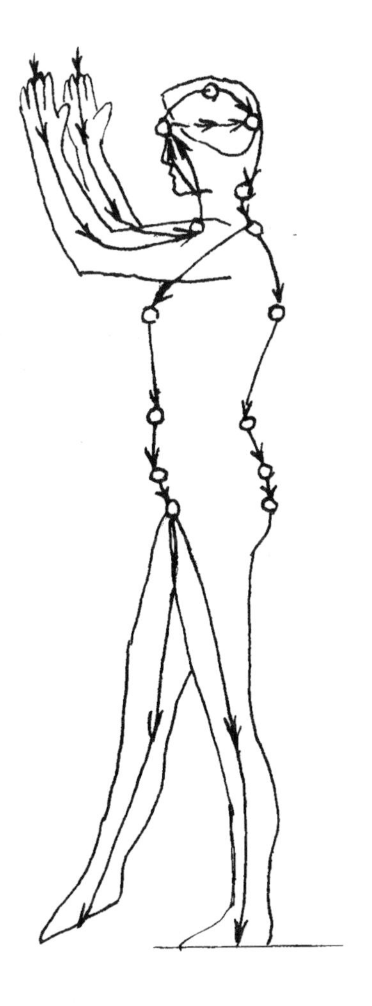

Figure 2. Increase of Bio-Energy

Ajna chakra, Sahasrara chakra (on the top of the head), and fills the back of the head (center of the memory). Use the self-suggestion: "My memory is strong; I remember everything that I need, and I can recall everything without any effort."
On the inhalation: more intensive flow enters the fingertips.
On the exhalation: energy goes through hands, shoulders, neck, and face filling brain, lowers through the spinal cord to coccyx touching the tops of all chakras (Ajna, Vishuddha, Anahata, Central, Manipura, Svadhisthana, and Muladhara) and strengthen them.
On the inhalation: again, intensive energy flow enters fingertips.
On the exhalation: energy flows through hands, shoulders, neck, face, head surface, back of the neck, and lowers down to all chakras filling internal organs, and energizing work of all organs and chakras.
On the inhalation: more intensive flow enters the fingertips.
On the exhalation: energy goes through hands, shoulders, neck, face, head, all the chakras, and all internal organs, fills legs and feet.

At the conclusion, when you receive energy on the inhalation, send it by a familiar scheme filling feet on the expiration (biologically active points, responsible for all internal organs, are located on feet). After the exercise put the palms together for 5 -6 seconds.

2. **Accumulation of the energy** (Figure 3).

This exercise is useful for those who practice energy healing, mas sage, and acupuncture; and also for people with weak nervous sys tem or living stressful lives. Usually, wasting energy takes place during stresses; and, an energetic imbalance results from this loss. If people would accumulate energy, then, during stressful situations, they could receive energy from their energetic accumulator. As a consequence, the balance might be maintained easily and they would not feel depleted of energy.
Stand or sit with raised hands (palms inward), facing north, and close your eyes. Do the exercise counting up to seven.
On the inhalation: send intensive flow of energy to the fingertips.
On the exhalation: with "one, two, three" count send energy through both hands to the solar plexus.
On the inhalation: send intensive flow to the fingertips.

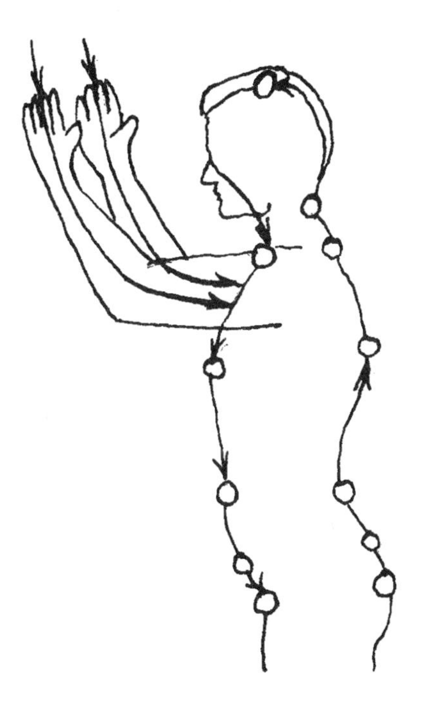

Figure 3. Accumulation of Bio-Energy

On the exhalation: on "four" send energy through hands to the solar plexus and lower it to the coccyx through the spinal column.
On the inhalation: send more energy to the fingertips.
On the exhalation: on "five" send energy through hands to the solar plexus, lower to the coccyx, and raise it through the spinal cord to the chest.
On the inhalation: again, send energy to the fingertips.
On the exhalation: on "six" send energy to the solar plexus through hands, lower it through the spinal cord to the coccyx (Manipura chakra), and then, raise it to the brain through all chakras on the spinal column.
On the inhalation: send energy to the fingertips.
On the exhalation: on "seven", the energy goes to the brain by a familiar scheme, and then back to the solar plexus.

In the beginning, you can spend up to 10 minutes doing exercises, nevertheless, as you advance, you will spend 30 seconds at the most. You can do these exercises in the morning and evening every day.

Bio-Energy, Relaxation and Stress

Before any bio-energetic work, it is important for energy-healers to learn methods of relaxation. Healers cannot perform energetic work in a stressful condition, or unable to cope with stress. In bio-energetics, a definition stress or distress means "negative stress, an accumulation of negative energy in the physical body, energetic imbalances in the bio-energy field, or throwing out of the body not only negative but positive vital energy as well."

On the physical level, stress response (or fight or flight response) occurs when people are involved in problems or a dangerous situation. The cerebral cortex (thinking organ) sends impulses to the hypothalamus (organ, responsible for stress responses). Then, the hypothalamus stimulates the sympathetic nervous system to make many changes in the body like heart rate, breathing rate, muscle tension, metabolism, and blood pressure. Reaction of the organism to outside problems is usually an increase of these components of well-being, as well as a decrease of blood flow from extremities (legs and arms) and the body's digestive system. The organism becomes ready to fight or run from the external event. If this condition of stress response continues uncontrolled, it can cause secretion of corticoids by adrenal glands which inhibit digestion, reproduction, growth, and tissue repair.

Negative stress, or distress, can cause stress-related illnesses and cardiovascular disease. Distress occurs when people encounter dangerous, difficult, painful, or unfair situations. However, stress response of the body can be useful in extreme cases when quick reactions, judgements, and bursts of energy help improve situations. At that time, people must turn off stress response to avoid permanent damage. As long as their minds receive threatening signals, they will keep the body aroused (stressful). Aroused states can increase occurrences of illnesses and weaknesses.

Relaxation response is a reaction of the organism to be free of stress, strong emotions, and tension. Relaxation response mechanisms can turn off stress responses in the brain when it stops sending signals to the organism about hazards. In minutes the metabolism, heart rate, breathing rate, muscle tension, and blood pressure return to normal levels. The underlying defensive processes of the organism also stop. In bio-energy healing, we will help healees achieve relaxation response and keep themselves in relaxed state.

Healers have lower frequencies of illness or weakness. They view difficult situations and threats of life from the positive side as challenges, or possibilities or examine themselves or opportunities for personal growth. They influence stressors in a positive way while gaining life experiences to neutralize distress. Healers make positive conclusions from negative experiences.

The effective ways to increase the ability to deal with distress involve integrating positive activities, moods, and thoughts into everyday life. Stopping to view a colorful landscape and smelling aroma of the garden can reduce stress. Regular exercise and relaxation, interesting social contacts and optimistic thinking, humor and play help maintain a positive attitude to live distress-free and healthy.

People have to acknowledge changes in their lives (negative or positive, as well as those forced on individuals or initiated by them). Without a possibility to improve changes, people have to adapt to them, and reestablish their lives accordingly. In order to avoid development of illnesses or symptoms after experiences of lengthy periods of stressful adaptations to new life conditions, people have to think about the meanings of each change, identify the experienced feelings, and choose the best way of adjustment to each change with positive decisions.

Healers have to be patient with selves, because the choices of personal coping strategies to deal with stress takes time. Each individual has to choose techniques that work effectively and easily. It is important to recognize and list the symptoms that cause distress as anxiety (in specific situations, personal relationships, and general anxiety), depression, powerlessness, poor self-esteem, anger, irritability, or fear, or physical symptoms (weakness, muscular tension, high blood pressure, all aches, ulcers, fatigue, insomnia, obesity, and job stress).

Healers should keep a journal. Describe your reactions to stressful situations and your feelings that cause stress. It is very important to start coping with stress by analyzing states of tensions, aches, and physical sensations. You can remember them, or you can make daily notes of physical and emotional irregularities which were proven useful. The notes will show how stressful events affect you, and how your organism reacts to them. If you find ways to release tensions and other stress symptoms from your body, you may experience greater wellness, joy, vitality, and increased energy. Although coping with stress is individual, by using special techniques, energy healers can manage stress level in different life situations, maximize their performance and satisfaction, and add more stimulating challenges, pleasure, and excitements to their lives.

Energy healers cope with distress using energetic methods. However, healers have to become positive mind oriented in everyday life. Remember, energy follows thought. It is a positive state of mind which controls energy flow, modulation of energy, and balancing the energy field. Mastery of manipulation with bio-energy brings health to the physical, mental, and emotional levels.

Before you will know bio-energetic methods of healing and energy management, you have to prepare self with regular relaxation techniques. All techniques to relieve stress are relaxation techniques that focus on relaxing the body and mind. To relieve a stress symptom such as general anxiety, you can practice these techniques to calm your body and emotions and relax your mind.

Relaxation exercise for deep muscle relaxation is practiced while lying down or sitting in a chair with the head supported. Keep each muscle or muscle's group tensed from five to seven seconds, and relaxed for twenty to thirty seconds. The use of mental statements when "untensing" can accelerate the state of deep relaxation of the body:

- I am letting the tension go.
- I am feeling calm and rested.
- Relax and smooth out muscles.

At first you can concentrate a particular group of muscles that are tense; then tense and relax groups of the muscles at one time to achieve deep muscle relaxation. Remember to notice contrasts between tension and relaxation. Return to the beginning position and relax. Clench your right fist tighter and tighter. Notice the tension. Keep it clenched, and, then, relax. Feel the looseness in your right hand and notice the contrast with tension. Repeat this procedure a few more times, and repeat it with the left fist, then with both fists at once. Bend the elbows and tense your biceps (muscles of upper arm). Tense them as hard as you can. Relax your muscles and straighten the arms. Wait until relaxation fully develops. Repeat this and all succeeding procedures at least once. Give special attention to your head. Tighten, relax, and smooth all parts of the face (forehead, eyes, jaws, scalp, and lips). Observe the difference between tension and relaxation. Notice that after these procedures all parts of your face are relaxed.

This group of procedures can be practiced at work, home or even while driving in a heavy traffic. Press your head back as far as you can (keep eyes on the same level). You will experience tension of the neck. Roll the head to the right then to the left. Now you experience another state of stress. Straighten your head and pull it forward, pressing the chin against your chest. Feel the tension in the throat and the neck. Bring your head backward and relax. Feel deep relaxation. Tension release brings deep relaxation gradually. Shrug your shoulders pulling them up and down. Keep the tension when your head is down between shoulders. Straighten and relax your shoulders.

Here is an another exercise which about relaxation of the

entire body. While lying down on the floor, breathe in deeply and hold in your breath. Feel the tension. Now exhale completely. Con tinue to breathe more freely and relax gradually. Next, tighten and hold your stomach, then relax. Repeat this for a few times. Relax the body.

Tighten your buttocks and thighs. Notice the tension then relax. Extend your legs as far as you can while lying on the floor and relax. Pull the toes downward (tension in the calves), and relax; then pull them the opposite way towards to the face and relax.

As relaxation deepens you will feel heaviness in your body. Concentrate on all the parts of the body, and experience the feeling of looseness and deep relaxation. With more practice you will feel the effect of relaxation much sooner. Do not hurry. The relaxation has to be complete and real (not seemingly). Mentally let the relaxation go deeper and deeper.

In the beginning of any practice or exercise try to help yourself with mental statements to accelerate conclusions, and with more practice you will be able to perform exercises without any statements, quickly and easily.

Psychic Health

Maintenance psychic health for healers in stressful times is a necessary part of maintenance overall physical health. Constant self-control, self-observation, self-feeling, and self-upbringing are very important parameters of the psychic health of the energy healer. Self-training can help suggest and control your psychic-physiological spheres. Doing the following exercises regularly will help you to maintain your own psychic health:

1. Sit down on the chair, put your hands on the knees, and close your eyes. The suggested form of thoughts are: " By counting up to ten, my hands become heavy, sticky to legs, and I am not able pull them away.

One - the hands begin to stick to legs.

Two - the hands become heavy.

Three-four - the hands are stuck.

Five-six - the hands are stuck with higher pressure.

Seven-eight - I cannot take them away. The more I try to pull them out, the more it becomes impossible to take them away.

Nine-ten - my hands strongly stick to the knees, and I cannot lift them up.

Now by counting up to five, my hands become lighter, more flexible, and movable. After this exercise any suggestion is realized by my mind.

One-two - the hands become lighter, movable, and are free from the knees.

Three-four - the hands become lighter, more active, and they do not stick anymore.

Five-six - the hands are free, active, and movable."

And right now in one minute, you can give any necessary and programmed statements to your mind.

2. The pose is the same. The suggested formula is: " By counting up to thirteen, my nervous system becomes strengthened, the body becomes light, and more active and fresh.

One-two - every cell of my central nervous system is strong, calm, and controlled.

Three-four - the nervous systems become stronger and calmer.

Five-six - my nervous system is strong, calm, and controlled by me.

Seven-eight - I am calm, strong, and self-confident person.

Nine-ten - my mental commands are realized with my mind in any moment.

Eleven-twelve - I always find right decisions, everywhere, even in extreme situations.

Thirteen - my mind is strong, calm, and controlled. At any moment my mental commands are always realized and everywhere.

By counting up to five, my body becomes fresh, light, and calm. I am finishing this exercise.

One - the body is light, fresh, and calm.

Two - hands and legs are light.

Three - the body is light.

Four - thoughts are delightful, fresh, and calm.
Five - my head is clean, fresh, and light."
Open your eyes, stand up, and take a walk.

Massage

Good massage can be used to release exhaustion and tension (after exercising or work), and to increase workability. Massage is known from ancient times and had been used in many countries among ancient Romans, Greeks, Chinese and Africans. Claudio Galen, a doctor of the gladiators, pointed out nine different kinds of massage, and described methods of caressing, rubbing, and kneading. He worked on methods of "morning" and "evening" massages. Roman and Greek warriors put massage into systems of physical education for warriors, and used it before and after arena performances. Massages use aromatic oils, swimming, or rubbing with sand.

The massage today includes caressing, rubbing, kneading, knocking, cracking, chopping, and so on. Massage is performed in the direction of blood flow in veins to relieve edemas and blood stagnation. Massage enlarges peripheral vessels moderately, and helps to increase the heart activity blood flow from organs.

In the morning you can do a hygienic self-massage with caressing, kneading, jolting, and active-passive movements to increase the tone of your body. Also before bedtime, massage can be done by caressing, kneading, and jolting easily and sensitively. Evening massages relieve nervous tensions accumulated during the day, contribute to the improvement of sleep.

It is important to accompany massage with morning or evening exercise. Here are some tips for better performing of self-massage. Pick a pose under which all muscles to be massaged are relaxed. The movement of the hand performing a self-massage goes in the direction of nearest lymph nodes. Arms are massaged in the direction from the wrists to nodes of the elbows and armpits, and legs to the knee nodes and groin. Do not massage lymph nodes. Do not massage inflamed places: abscesses, cuts, thrombus, and varicose veins. Ask your doctor if you can have a massage.

The massage of the face brings pleasure. You can do

sensitive movements following facial nerves in the direction from the center to the temples: under eyes' apples, above the brows, on the forehead, and from the ends of lips to the temples. The surface of the head is massaged in the direction of hair growth by both hands at the same time. Fingers should browse, twitch, tie up the skin, and caress calmly. In the morning and during the daytime, you can tap the fingers lightly on the scalp. The massage has to bring pleasure, so do not do it longer than five minutes. Intensity and satisfaction depend on degree of exhaustion and emotional state. In a case of high exhaustion, or nervous excitement massage move ments have to be done effortlessly. Morning massage may be done intensively.

Self-massage of the legs begins with working on the muscles of feet, the calves, thighs, and hips. You can massage foot and ankle while you sit on a firm sofa. Keep massaged leg bent and other leg straight while lying on the sofa. Muscles of the calf area are massaged, when both legs are bent (for relaxed calves, put feet on a roll of blanket, or pillow). In the evening you can massage raised legs while you lie on the bed. Massage of the hips' muscles can be done using several positions, depending on kinds of massaged muscles. In any case massaged muscles must be relaxed.

After legs, you may massage muscles of buttocks and lower back. This can be done by kneading and energetic jolting (shaking). You can massage an area of lower back with both hands (by fingers or fists). You can combine rubbing the lower back with flexions, extensions, and rotations of the body. It is better to massage muscles of the chest when lying on the back while using caressing, jolting and rubbing.

Self-massage of arms is done, when you sit, stand or lie down. At first you can massage fingers, hands, and wrists using rubbing. When you massage upper arms, work on different muscles (biceps and triceps) separately, and finish on the elbows (caressing and kneading). When you are working on the head or neck, you can lie down or sit at the table. Put elbows on the table in order to prevent exhaustion in the arm muscles, to relieve tension of shoulder muscles. First, massage back of the head, nape, neck and shoulders, by caressing and kneading the muscles with the ring finger. You can massage hills behind the ears with thumbs making rotational movements.

You have to be careful with massaging the throat, because the neck has the main arteries and veins. Nevertheless, massaging the throat is effective to relieve exhaustion that occurs from continuous brain activity; also as a result of long sittings in fixed positions of head and spine when vein blood flow from the head decreases. In this case you can pull the back of the head downward, lifting the chin, and caress from up to down on both sides of the throat along the blood vessels. You have to work carefully when you massage clavicles and shoulders because those areas are full of painful massage points.

Chapter Three

Special Tools in Bio-Energetic Healing

Before learning how to perform energy healing, everyone has to prepare the mind with special techniques and exercises. To master any bio-energetic work your mental attitude must be changed. You have to be able to consciously control your bio-energy. Your bio-energy follows your thought. Your conscious mind and bio-energy may help you to live "energetic", fulfilling life, and proper management of your bio-energy may bring better health to you and your family.

There are a few special tools which may promote the development and mastery of a special mind state and bio-energetic ability: meditation, positive thinking, visualization, and self-hypnosis. In this chapter you will also learn about how to perform human energetic protection and distant increase of the energy in another person.

Meditation

Healers achieve a special state of consciousness, spiritual knowledge, and self-realization through meditation. Eastern mystics consider meditation as highly sophisticated, and a private method to observe nature, the universe, and to achieve constant awareness to perceive a new reality of the inner self, and thus, the Universe. Eastern mystics consider humans the whole and identify themselves with the ultimate reality, and Divine who controls everything from within the body.

With meditation techniques require the mind to be absolutely quieted, not thinking. Meditation helps to shift awareness from the rational to the intuitive mode of consciousness. Energy healers have to develop the ability to attain meditative mode of consciousness. For someone it seems a completely new experience. Nevertheless, any bio-energy work demands a healer to be in meditative state of mind.

In scientific terms, our brains elicit four types of electrical brain-wave- frequencies: alpha, beta, theta, and delta. The slowest brain waves are delta (deep sleep). Rapid brain-wave frequencies are beta (rational, detail-oriented thinking). Stress and negative thinking or emotions can appear while the brain is in the beta state. Most adults live and work at the beta-wave frequency or typical working condition. At beta (brain alert and logical) inspiration or creative activity cannot occur.

Next to delta, slow theta waves appear before sleep. They are associated with drowsiness and rapid assimilation of new information. Theta brain-wave frequencies appear in deeply relaxed or day-dreaming states. When meditating or practicing yoga people can control their mental states, and manipulate their brain waves producing a memory-triggering creative theta state. Mental phenomena such as hypnagogic imagery, creative thoughts, integrative experiences, and spontaneous memories may be brought with theta state. In theta state, the physical body is deeply relaxed but mind is extremely alert and lucid. Inspiration or insight appears while in theta state of mind.

Alpha frequencies are higher than theta, and less than beta. Alpha produces relaxation. The alpha state occurs when people enter meditative states (theta replaces alpha activity). The meditative state can also be named alpha and theta state. At first mind goes empty, and then the feeling is replaced by creative imagination or day dreaming. Inner healing of the physical body is accelerated in alpha and theta state. And healing by bio-energy can be done while the healer and healee appear to be in this state. Alpha and theta state brings harmonious balance between left hemisphere activity (rational thinking), and right hemisphere activity of the brain (creativity) and a balanced state of whole-brain integration while physical body is deeply relaxed. This is extremely beneficial to reach a higher level of mental powers and reorientation toward life. In this state the mind works at high intellectual levels, and it is accompanied with creativity, euphoria, intuition, and feeling of being oneness with the universe.

In many forms of meditation, this quieting of the rational mind is achieved by concentrating one's attention on a single thing or sound (breathing, mantra, or a visual image). One method of concentration of your consciousness on one thing or thought at the time of exercise is not easy to do, because the mind thinks all the time, recalling unexpected and unusual thoughts. Also it does not want concentrate on one thing or it is distracted. People need meditation because they think about their problems all the time. They need to learn how to relax and forget about them for a while. The ability to stay concentrated or distracted for a while is a mastery that can be achieved by frequent practice. When you can stay concentrated, you are able to control your physical, mental, and, later, even energetic state.

In the beginning of practice of meditation, if you experience your mind starting to wander, try to return your consciousness to the object of meditation and wave away those thoughts like clouds. When mind concentrates on one chosen thought or object, it is not possible to worry, fear, and hate. When practiced regularly, your body can learn about the way of ridding anxiety, depression, fear, hostility and other stressful emotions. You will learn to manage strong and habitual emotions, and let them pass without any trace. You will be able to maintain equilibrium in your life without unhealthful emotions.

Meditation itself is successfully used in prevention and treatment of high blood pressure, heart problems, migraines, diabetes, and arthritis. You can meditate when you experience pain. Usually people's reaction to pain is building tightness around that area. This produces even more harm. The better way to deal with pain is to soften pain areas, and consciously and compassionately relax. As you focus on discomfort or pain, try to soften the area. If muscles tighten, try to relax them. If you cannot achieve muscle relaxation, try again. Try to breathe deeply and focus on the sensations inside you. Is there any tension? Release it.

Whenever you need to release tension, tiredness, pain,

or stressful emotions, find a comfortable posture, center yourself, and take several deep breaths. Begin your meditation and focus on sensations of inner discomfort, scanning your body to see if muscles are tightening. Find ways to calm self down repeating gently "Re lax", or "Let it go more". Later, you can scan your body for tension, take several deep breaths, and relax.

It is better to start meditation with breath-counting. In the beginning, just simply count each deep inhalation to ten, then start over with "one". Observe what is going on within yourself, wait until all current sensations are gone; however, return the consciousness to the counting. When you open your eyes at the end of your meditation, you will realize you feel much more relaxed than you did before meditating.

For your meditation you can choose any sitting postures with crossed legs, or Yoga postures where you can sit straight. To find the balance of the body, you can rock slightly from side to side. Breathe through your nose. Touch the palate of your mouth with your tongue. All you need is a quiet place, comfortable pose, and emptiness of the stomach (not less then two hours after eating).

Staying centered or grounded is an important part of meditation and bio-energetic work. Closing your eyes, or discentering your vision, render centering physically and psychologically, finding inside yourself internal reference of stability. The centering is an act of self-searching, understanding of own being and relationship to the universe. Through centering you can be aware of dynamics of your own consciousness and body. In the beginning of practice, pay attention to the full abdominal breathing. Breathing will become deeper unconsciously with practice.

Maintenance of passive attitude during meditation helps to achieve meditative state. For beginners to have a lot of thoughts and few moments of clear consciousness is natural, nevertheless, try to diffuse and become oneness with the universe by gradually mastering switching the consciousness. Starting with a few minutes, you will find meditation comfortable from 20 to 30 minutes.

The most common form of meditation throughout the world is "mantra" meditation. "Mantra" is a use of any words or syllables. The most effective "mantra" is "OM"(universal mantra, that connects our souls with universe). Pronounce it as a music note,

"A-A-O-M-M-M..." Let the mantra find its own rhythm as you repeat it over and over again. Chant your mantra mentally or aloud, which ever is more relaxing to you. Listen to inner self. Instead of inner voice, your consciousness has to chant the mantra.

You may meditate when you eat, walk, or go to bed. Any simple activity can become a meditation when you try to focus your attention on it continuously. Concentrate on every action and every sensation involved in the activity. You could practice concentrating when you shave, brush your teeth, wash dishes, and so on. As thoughts occur, note them, and go back and renew concentration on chosen object: mantra, counting, or releasing of tension.

Self-Hypnosis

Self-hypnosis is an experience of thoughts and images. Self-hypnosis itself has been found effective to treat symptoms of insomnia, chronic pains, headaches, muscular tensions, minor anxieties, indecision, and agitation. Do not be afraid of self-hypnosis or resist it, because everything you do automatically is done with self-hypnosis. Following instructions is important performance.

Sit in a comfortable position. The key word or phrase you can choose the one which is the opposite of your state or problem. Against anxiety you can use the key phrase, "Calm and heavy, and deeply relaxed." Key words help induce self-hypnosis quickly and effectively. Breathe deeply from the abdomen, and feel the spreading sense of relaxation as you exhale. When you start to relax your muscles, pronounce key phrases like "loose and relaxed", "heavier and deeply relaxed", and "calm and relaxed." Imagine any special place where you can feel safe and peaceful, and involve all five senses. To deepen your state use phrases such as "drifting deeper and deeper", "feeling more peaceful and calm", "drifting into the relaxed state." Repeat everything until any suggestion begins to induce relaxation. Use creative imagery to help your muscles relax.

Giving positive self-suggestions for changing some reactions, problems or uncertain feelings of the organism is useful in everyday life. The suggestions have to be direct and in a positive form, and made for immediate future. They are repeated a few times. Instead of negative and uncertain phrases, such as: "I won't be anxious", and "I try to be relaxed", you must use positive, permissive, or com mand phrases that work best for you, such as "I will be calm and in control", "I can feel relaxed and refreshed soon", and "Relax deeper and entirely." At the time when you perform hypnosis, you can let your strong emotions reach their peak, and then go into state of the relaxation. When you are able to turn your emotions and mental states on and off during hypnosis, you will gain enormous control over your life.

You can use self-hypnosis when you become obsessed with negative thoughts, feel fear, fatigue, chronic pain, have constant anger or guilt, low self-esteem, lack of motivation, insecurity, anxiety, chronic muscle tension, or other negative symptoms. For better results, in the beginning of the session of self-hypnosis, always define your problem and goal. Identify and try to eliminate any external or internal factors that may be contributing to your problem, and create your own problem and suggestions that incorporate the ideas to reinforce your desired behavior; or to change reaction of your body.

You can use your key phrases whenever you feel tense or discomfort. Or, you can think memorized stress-coping thoughts that helped you earlier. Stress-coping thoughts report that your body has no need for arousal - they can relax and help to calm the body. In the middle of any stressful situation, you can start mentioning to yourself a series of statements like, "Stay calm... Relax... I will deal with this... I am going to be all right... I can do this... Breathe deeply... I did it...Relax now..."

It is very important in any bio-energetic work to be able to give yourself direct mental or verbal commands, such as: "I can heal," "My energy flows freely," "I perform energy healing," "I bring healing with my energy."

Positive thinking

One important condition for energy healers is positive thinking. Positive thinking is an effective way to achieve mastery of bio-energy healing. Maintenance of positive energy level in healer's own bio-energy field reduces stress and emotional tension and of others. Positive emotions and feelings and positive mental attitude can prove the quality of people's lives, and heal their bodies of illnesses and stresses.

On the other hand, negative emotions and feelings bring poisoning toxins to the organism. Strong negative emotions such as anger, spite, envy, jealousy, and fear make the endocrine system accumulate poisons in blood. Anxiety, depression, and doubt can also cause poisoning of the blood. Passive and lengthy negative emotions are even more dangerous for health than active, sudden and momentary negative emotions. Negative emotions shorten the span of a life.

Treatment of physical symptoms with positive thoughts and statements was popularized in France a century ago, and it still has a strong power to overcome unwanted states (stress, tension, and unhappiness). Thoughts and feelings make up reality and add color to it. So unhappiness brings gray world and reality. To change a gray world and to overcome the feeling of unhappiness, anxiety, or tension, one needs to refocus the mind on positive, healing thoughts.

When people predict that something is going happen to them, more likely it will happen, because negative thoughts will be reflected in their unconscious. Moreover, there could be developed psychosomatic illnesses (70% of all illnesses are psychosomatic, or caused by mental stress). Psychosomatic illnesses worsen when given special attention. Instead of paying direct attention to pain or illness, you can tell every time a negative thought occurs, " It will be better than I think." When a wish of any desired condition is established in the mind, somehow the unconscious mind leads to realization a wish to come true, not magically, but programmed.

Besides healing illnesses, positive attitudes help withstand troubles and problems, make correct decisions, and overcome obstacles. Do not focus on negative events, but try to find out a positive perspective to fulfill things. For example, individuals should understand that they need to read more or think more of others in order to find ways of perfect communication. Because thoughts of individuals are either positive or negative, they are reflected in their social or asocial behaviors. People should observe and conceive the world around them and their inner worlds with positive perceptions.

Healers should have "a positive mind state" before they begin practice bio-energy healing. Healers communicate with other people giving them energy. "Negative" energy cannot bring healing but damage, and it is destructive for both a healer and a healee. Healing energy is "a positive" energy which sent by "a positive mind."

Visualization

Visualization is a powerful tool for bio-energy healing which will prepare you to perceive energy flowing, the control of energy, the transfer of energy, and healing. The power of imagination far exceeds the power of will. For example, if you find that loosen state is difficult to achieve in the relaxation technique, you can imagine the relaxation spreading within you, and visualize yourself relaxed in a comfortable position.

The mind controls all thoughts and internal occurrences. With powerful imagination, you increase your mind power greatly and help your physical body to live better. Your developed ability to visualize will manage your thoughts and images in the right way for your body, energy, and increase your ability to heal and maintain bio-energy.

Visualization should be an everyday practice. Visualization may be considered a natural ability of the mind. Daydreams, memories, mental images, and inner voices are many kinds of visualization. When the eyes are closed, visual cortex of the brain is able to influence physical and emotional states, and connect visual brain to the involuntary nervous system. Try visualizations or mental impressions that you create consciously in order to relieve stress and achieve body relaxation as well. Besides help in relaxing the body, visualization may develop your creativity and improve your life. You may guide and consciously employ your visualizations for bettering yourself and your life, and your ability to manipulate bio-energy will enhance the healing process.

Here are few techniques of different types of visualization that will guide you to visualize effectively:

- You can close your eyes,
- Relax,
- Empty your mind,
- Visualize a pleasurable scene, such as you are in the woods, birds sing, sun shines through emerald crowns of the trees, and

aroma scents are surrounding you. And when you will ask, "Why cannot I relax?" The answer may appear in your consciousness about the primary reason of your stress.

In addition, you can create an image (involve all senses) of the field you wish to improve. Program mentally the result you want to reach. Practice it daily, and visualize it when you perform tasks. By visualizing the perfect outcome, your consciousness will be programmed to achieve it in reality. Give yourself mental affirmations in the present.

Or, you can create a healthy image of an organ that is painful or weak at first, lead its visualized image up into a blue sunny sky, bathing in a warm morning sunlight. For example, imagine a liver being caressed by white clouds, cleansed of toxins, filled with vitality, fresh air, and ready for work again. Bring it carefully back by hands in the place in the body. Relax, and think how powerful it is now.

When you are visualizing, try to find a quiet place. Scan your body in order to discover tensed places, and relax them. Form mental impressions using all five senses for more effective visualization. And help the imagination process by mental positive statements such as "I relax at will", "Tension is leaving me", or "I am in harmony with myself."

When you close your eyes with palms, try to visualize black color in about three minutes, and you will achieve the relaxation state (very effective technique to perform when you are out of time). Visualize any tension-image of your choice and let it soften and fade, creating relaxation and harmony. For example, the dark tunnel ends with light colorful valley; or any unpleasant smell like ammonia fades into soft exotic fragrance. And apply these tension-images to the tensed muscles; those determined by scanning the body to achieve relaxation (you can help with words of affirmation every time you visualize). At first concentrate on tensed muscles, and then visualize images of tension fading into pleasure images.

In the beginning of practice with healing energy, healers use visualized images of energy flows and chakras. They visualize the whole process of healing, and their bio-energy follows their thoughts. The images also help to perform energy modulation and transfer it to another person.

Distant Increase of the Energy in Another Person

Sometimes you will be faced with the need of transfer your energy to a person with weak energy. Before healing by your energy, first do the exercise for the accumulation of your own energy to avoid self-depletion (Chapter Two).

Put the person in front of you with their back facing north. Raise your hands.Imagine taking the vector of the energy from your solar plexus, and mentally sending it to the wrists of that person. Make a pass of energy with your palms from the head to feet of the person: Put your hands together over the head of the person, and conduct a pass from both sides in his or her body. Make a pass for three times.

Imagine that every one of your cells passes an intensive flow of energy. Give the command to the mind: "My energy will easily be taken, transformed, and assimilated by the person." And, then, in 7 - 8 seconds, rub the palms and pass the energy with your hands by clockwise movements approaching the head (3 seconds) at a distance 4-6 inches to the person's torso and hands (6 seconds). Pass the energy to legs (work hands near the solar plexus, and send the energy with three passes along the legs).

When sending energy, in the beginning it is better to imagine that the person is floating in your healing energy, and it brings the person cheerfulness, health, and joy.

In conclusion, secure your energy to avoid blowing it away, because the person's organism can only absorb your energy into its own gradually, not all at once.

For this reason, put three middle fingers of the right hand together. Pass a vertical line from the top of person's head to the end of the torso with fingers at the distance of 2 - 4 inches above the body. Then pass one horizontal line from left to right, on the brows' level, and another line - from left nipple to the right nipple. After that lower the line about 45 degrees to the appendix. The fastening can be done in 3 - 6 - 9 times. This scheme is for females. For males - make horizontal lines from right to left, and lower the line to under 45 degrees to the opposite side of the body (Figure 4).

After work, restore your own energy doing Exercise 1, increasing your level of the energy (Chapter Two).

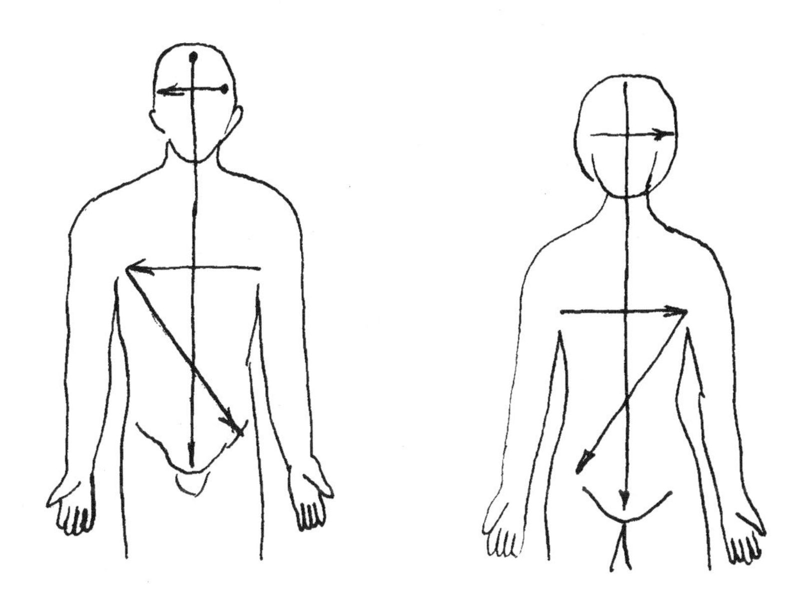

Figure 4. Securing Energy

In extreme cases, when you have to give first aid, hold the biologically active points in the hands of the person (between thumb and point finger) tightly, send the energy through your right hand to the left hand of the person, and mentally visualize energy. Give the mental command: "My energy goes through the left hand of the healee, through their heart, through their right hand, and enters my left hand."

Recharge this energy a few times between 10 - 15 seconds.

By promoting the cycle of two bio-systems, you help the person with weak energy to normalize their energy condition.

Human Energetic Protection

When we communicate with other people, our energy fields interfere with each other. Sometimes the influence of bio-energy systems can be negative, because the energy systems of various types of people may differ in strength, quality, and quantity of energy. The definition of "a bad eye" is the interference between two bio-energy systems when negative energetic information (it may occur unconsciously) from stronger bio-energy system is transferred into another system. To be safe from a "bad eye", energy depletion, and energetic "damage", we need to know how we can protect ourselves from influences of other human energy systems. It is very important to know what to do, and how to secure self. Many human energy systems feed on energies of other human beings (energy vampirism).

To protect yourself energetically, you can create a powerful bio-energy protection system. Here is the exercise for this purpose.

Stand facing north. Raise your hands above the head, and, on the count of seven get energy in the wrists from air. Press your fingers together making fists and grabbing energy from space seven times (Figure 5).

Bend the left arm at the elbow less than 45 degrees, and put it on your side with palm inward above the solar plexus. Raise the right hand keeping fingers apart in front of your face between 5 - 7 inches. Give yourself a mental command: "Right now I will create seven energetic cylinders which will provide a very strong energetic protection, and make it impossible to break through."

Figure 5. Bio-Energy Protection

Make seven circled movements above your head clockwise with the right hand, clockwise down, and mentally imagine that you create cylinders around yourself: first, second, third, and so on until you hit seven. Join the fingers together and pass the right hand over a hole at the joint of cylinders down to the floor. This draws each cylinder together, and, then, mentally connect them to your energy field.

From time to time you have to change the cylinders (repeat the procedure all over again), because of accumulated negative information.

To dissemble the cylinders, put the fingers of the right hand together. Imagine that your energy opens cylinders by leading the hand from the top down to the floor. When all seven cylinders are opened, begin movement counterclockwise with your hand over your head. Mentally remove each cylinder. After each procedure shake the right hand, and after the last one, shake both hands three times ridding yourself of negative information.

After this create a new energetic protection system following the same procedure.

Chapter Four

Yoga for Achievement and Harmony of Inner-Self

There is no any other discipline more helpful in achieving knowledge of inner- self, and harmony with the world than Yoga. Bio-energy knowledge of methods of mind and body healing cannot be completed without studying Yoga.

Basic Hatha-Yoga is a practical and complex method of developing a healthier body, mind and psyche. Pranayama is the teaching of proper breathing. By studying Hatha-Yoga exercises, and poses, and Pranayama exercises, we learn how to breathe properly, meditate, be centered, relaxed, gain life energy, massage the internal organs, keep the body healthy and flexible, and accelerate removal of toxins.

There are three types of exercises: "**Asanas**" (or poses), **dynamic**, and **breathing**.

The Asanas are poses that influence energetic centers and systems of the body. Certain asana influences specific nerve centers. With the system of complex asanas we positively influence the endocrine system, help every cell and organ of the body. We recommend that you to perform the system of poses keeping in mind that any illness is a dysfunction of normal activity.

Yogis' asanas help keep elasticity and mobility of physical bodies. When people perform everyday work, or do chores, they move joints with little breadth. And if they ignore exercises or sports, they can lose the flexibility, elasticity, and mobility of the spine, joints, tendons, and muscles. By the time the "working angle" of joints decreases, people cannot perform deep inclinations, situps, or wide turns of the body. This immobility can lead to illnesses like arthritis and bursitis. To prevent losing flexibility, people can add exercises for their joints and tendons.

Every day, and for life, you need to do rotational movements of the head, arms, legs, and body; bending the body to the sides, and forward, and extensions of the back; also situps and pushups with maximum amplitude of moving in order to maintain mobility of the entire body. Try to work all joints as well as the spinal column. Repeat every exercise (with every group of joints) 6-10 times. Start exercising by warming up. Begin each exercise with small breadth and go to your extreme "working angle" gradually to avoid a trauma.

Dynamic Yoga exercises help accelerate the removal of toxins from the body. Every system of the body is affected with toxins. One of the reasons for having illnesses is the presence of toxins in the body. Today, people are exposed to chemicals, pesticides, additives in food, and anesthetics in greater concentrations (sources of toxins) than at any other time in history.

People's organisms have to struggle with constant invasion of toxins, because processes to removal toxins are complicated and take more time than the assimilation and the absorption of nutrients. Toxins and chemicals penetrate membranes and accumulate in intercellular space. Toxins enter lymphatic and blood vessels, where veinous blood carries toxins to the organs of elimination. This transit of toxins through millions of cells is difficult to complete without activity of vibrated cells, muscular contractions, exertions that occur during walking, running, and jumping.

During evolution nature did not find more effective way to clean up cells and intercellular space of toxins than the use of those forces of muscular contractions and forces of jolting due to the body movements. When muscles contract, they compress veins, accelerate a flow of venous blood to the heart, and provide impulses that help blood to eliminate toxins. We can observe how pets stretch their bodies after waking up. When the body stretches, muscles are contracted. The body needs stretching after waking up in the morning. During the sleep, heart muscles help move venous blood with wastes and toxins; however, this help is not enough to remove toxins. The weakening of the body is due not to effects of illness, but to the transgression of the entire metabolism, because of the accumulation of toxins. Removal of toxins from cells and intercel lular spaces is a process requiring constant vibration of cells by nerve impulses, and occurs during exercising or moving which pro vides contractions of muscles. When people do not exercise or move efficiently (stretching, aerobics, running, walking, and dancing), their bodies gradually decline.

In the morning, the best way to help the body to accelerate the removal of the toxins is doing the following exercise. People can do this exercise, even if they cannot run, or walk. You can do it while you take a shower.

Pull the heels up off the floor a half an inch, and put them back down sharply but not painfully. Repeat this motion 30 times, then rest for 5-10 seconds. Later, repeat 30 times more. At the same time, you can bend arms keeping forearms parallel to the floor surface, and bend your hands as if you held a ball. When putting the heels up, shove your wrists forward then pull them back. You can do it with a second interval. You can do this exercise a few more times during the day. People who stand or sit for long periods of time will benefit from doing this exercise; it prevents thrombosis (blood clotting) and heart problems.

Healthy functioning of the body is possible when the intake of food products and removal of products of digestion and activity of the cells of the body are balanced. Toxins occur in the organisms as a result of stress and anxiety. When a young person has the energy enough to detoxify the organism through its organs (intestines, kidneys, skin, and lungs), the chances for imbalance small. But between 30-35 years of age the body, if not trained by special exercises, lacks the energy to remove toxins.

Besides help in the toxin elimination, dynamic Yoga exercises also help to build a beautiful and strong body.

Breathing Yoga exercises help gain life energy - prana. People often think that they can breathe properly. But sometimes people do not breathe correctly for their whole life. Nevertheless, right breathing is the key to gain energy and vitality. Proper breathing influences all bodily processes including brain activity and digestion, and provides oxygen to muscles, organs, and tissues; in addition it removes toxins and wastes. Yogis developed their teachings about proper breathing about six thousand years ago. Some of ancient techniques can help people to maintain health.

When you wake up after stretching your body, you can lie down on your back and relax your muscles. Then inhale deeply while pushing out the chest. After this try to pull the diaphragm down while exhaling and the diaphragm will massage the intestines, kidneys, liver, spleen, and pancreas. At the same time the stomach applies pressure on the intestinal cavity. You can repeat these movements many times to learn how to move the diaphragm up and down. This exercise helps massage internal organs and increases activity. This pressure will help squeeze toxins and wastes out of cells.

Here is another exercise. Inhale deeply while lying on the back then push out the stomach which moves the diaphragm. Delay your breathing for 3-5 seconds, and start to exhale air in small portions, and pulling it through tightly closed lips. This exercise internally massages all organs. The same massage occurs at moments of laughter. Laughter has been considered important for well-being since ancient times.

Physiologically the massage of organs of the abdominal cavity increases the flow of blood to the heart. The contractions of the abdominal muscles help in relieve heart problems. The heart cavity is in the same space as the lungs and the diaphragm. The diaphragm, due to its sensitivity to emotions moves closer to the heart and lessens the heart space. The brain regulates volumes of blood entering the heart. If the amount of blood is less than necessary to sustain life, the rhythms and intensity of heart impulses have to increase. The increase of the heart beat occurs with every move of the diaphragm which decreases the space in the heart cavity. These conditions can even cause heart attack. If you feel an accelerated heart beat rate, inhale and push out the stomach for 2-3 seconds. This provides more space to the heart cavity and (repeat all over for 3-4 times).

Breathing exercises help develop elasticity of the diaphragm, which massages internal organs, increases the volume of the heart cavity, and decreases chance of developing of heart problems. We will learn how to load ourselves with bio-energy using yoga exercises.

Conditions for Yoga Exercises

1. Perform Yoga poses in the morning or in the evening before eating on an empty stomach.
2. The room must have fresh air.
3. No smoking allowed in the room.
4. No talking before Yoga exercises in the room.
5. It is better to do Yoga alone.
6. Do exercises on the floor or on a firm rug.
7. Wear relaxed and stretchy clothing.

Lower Breathing

Expiration - all internal organs draw in. Pause on expiration - 1 - 2 seconds. Deep breath - push the stomach out (slowly, gently, as if drinking the air). Start breathing with this technique putting hands on the stomach. This breathing exercise is ideal to prevent asthma. Lower breathing of the diaphragm massages internal organs.

Dead Man Pose

Lie down on the floor and keep your hands on the body (see Figure 6). Relax with the following techniques (relaxation goes from down to up):

1. Toes, feet, ankles, legs, thighs, hips are relaxed, warm and heavy.
2. Lower back, middle back, and chest are relaxed.
3. Heart beats calmly and evenly. Liver, bladder, spleen are relaxed.
4. Hands, fingers, wrists, arms, and shoulders are relaxed. Hands and arms become warm and heavy.
5. Neck is relaxed.
6. Face is relaxed. Jaws are hung down. Eyes are relaxed. Narrate to yourself: "I am a bird, sky is blue, blue. I am alone flying in the sky."

You can do this exercise for 10-15 minutes or less.

Therapeutic effect. Influences the nervous system, heart, circulatory system; and it is ideal rest for all other systems of the body.

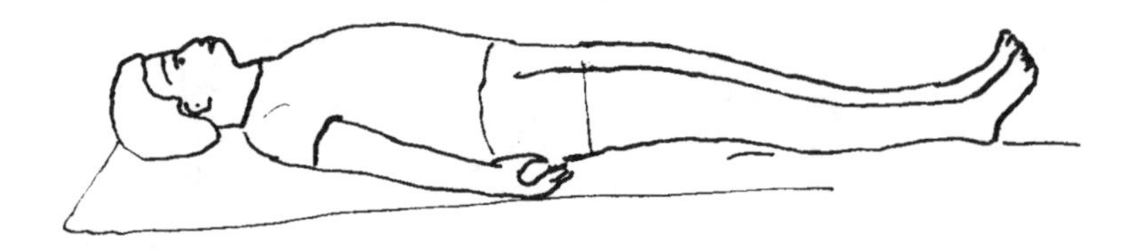

Figure 6. Dead Man Pose

Figure 7. Diamond Pose

Diamond Pose

Sit on the ankles. Head, neck, and torso are kept in straight line. Place hands on the knees (Figure 7).

Therapeutic effect. Strengthens knees, improves digestion and self-confidence.

Exercise after Awakening

When you awaken in the morning, suggest to self the feeling of joy and happiness: "I am happy, cheerful, and joyful. I will do exercises right now to strengthen my health, and fill myself with energy and life power."

Lie down on your back on the bed, keep legs together, put hands alongside the body.

1. Pull the left ankle forward, hold for five seconds, and then relax.

2. Pull the right ankle forward, hold for five seconds, and then relax.

3. Extend both legs, and go back initiate position.

You can do this exercise 2-3 times a day (less than 5).

Therapeutic effect. Normalizes blood circulation, sympathetic nervous system, and relieves lower back pain.

Snake Pose

Lie with your face down on the floor, keep your hands on the shoulder's level with palms down (Figure 8). Concentrate your attention on the thyroid while extending the body, and inhale. Keep your attention moving to the coccyx (lowest part of spinal column). During exhalation, the attention goes back to the thyroid.

Make a sharp expiration. With a deep breath, raise your head as high as possible. Arrange your shoulders, strengthen back muscles, and elevate your shoulders without help from hands (use hands to avoid sliding). Keep your abdomen on the floor. In the upper position with your head and shoulders up, you can keep buttocks' muscles very tight for a moment, stop breathing for 7-12 seconds and relax.

Figure 8. Snake Pose

With a slow expiration return to the beginning position and relax.

Therapeutic effect. Influences abdomen organs and relieves cystitis.

Palm Pose

Keep your feet about one foot apart. Keep the head, neck and back in a straight line. Concentrate your attention on the vertebral column (you can do this exercise anywhere without raising hands, but with concentration on the spinal column). Exhale. With a deep breath gently raise your hands, stretch your vertebral column, and stand on your toes. Fix this position for five seconds.

Therapeutic effect. Tonic for your body.

Roll Pose

Do this exercise on a rug, because "things" absorb energetic information of individuals.

Sit down. Pull your knees against the body. Let the ankles touch the buttocks while keeping feet together and hugging legs with hands (left hand grabbing right wrist - for males, and for females - the opposite).

Sharply roll the body backward and return it to the beginning position quickly, and repeat it 10 to 100 times. For the beginners, 10 times are enough. Breathing - free style.

Therapeutic effect. Makes the vertebral column flexible and strong; helps to prevent illnesses of the brain; and it is good for gas relief and inducing sleep.

This is the only pose you can perform a few minutes before going to bed.

Yoga Mudra

Sit in the Diamond pose. Pull your hands back and put them over the spine. Lock the hands as in the Roll pose (Figure 9). Concentrate your attention on the solar plexus and abdomen. Exhale and slowly pull your body forward trying to touch the floor with your forehead, and then chin. Do not remove buttocks away from

Figure 9. Yoga Mudra

ankles. Stay in this position as long as possible. Exhale and return to the first position.

Therapeutic effect. It is effective for removal of fat. Excellent for strengthening the spinal column and maintaining self-confidence.

Meditative Pose to Induce a Positive Mood

Sit in the Diamond pose and breathe normally. Concentrate your consciousness on positive, optimistic, mental images for 3-5 minutes. Relax your muscles and think only about happiness, joy, and beauty and kindness. At the conclusion of this exercise you will be in a good mood and have positive thoughts to maintain health.

Strengthening Abdomen Muscles

1. Stand straight and look forward. Keep feet together, hands down, and spine straight. Exhale through the nose, and pull abdomen (stomach) down as far as possible. Inhale and push abdomen out to the extreme. In the beginning you can do this five times. When you master the technique, 50 times will be enough.

2. Everything is the same, but the torso is bent over 45 degrees with hands on the lower back.

3. Keep feet apart about one foot. Bend knees, and put your hands on the knees (Fisherman Pose). Look forward. Keep your shoulders straight. Perform the abdomen movements shown in Exercise 1.

4. Position is the same as in Exercise 3. Do abdomen movements and exhale through the nose. Stop breathing momentarily and keep a pause as long as you can. Then slowly inhale and relax.

Therapeutic effect. The exercises stimulate nerves in the solar plexus, help remove abdomen fat, strengthen lower abdomen muscles, stimulate nerves that influence movements of the intestines, and assist intestines to work well.

Caution: People with heart and circulatory problems should consult with a physical therapist if the exercises are suitable for them. People with stomach problems should do them slowly and carefully.

Full Yoga Breathing

There are three types of breathing: **upper**, **middle**, and **lower**. The knowledge how to breathe properly teaches you how to load the body with cosmic energy - prana.

Upper chest breathing occurs with cooperation of the upper part of the lungs. When inhaling, scapulas are lifted, and shoulders and ribs move up. The upper chest is filled with air. The air does not enter the alveoli (microscopic air sacs) in the lungs where oxygen enters the blood and carbon dioxide leaves. Yogis think that this type of breathing is not complete. They use this type of breathing in exercises for developing mobility of the chest. If people always breathe in this manner, they may develop respiratory or other illnesses.

Lie down on the back. Keep palms on the lower back with elbows on the rug. Bend your spine and chest up. Draw abdomen in and keep it tight. Take a deep breath and expand the chest to the extreme; pause for a moment and exhale slowly. You can do this exercise up to 12 times.

When we breathe by middle breathing, we fill the middle part of the lungs with air. Ribs are raised, the chest is expanded, and the diaphragm and the abdomen become mobile. However, this type of breathing is superficial.

The third type is abdomen breathing. We can breathe using the lower part of the chest and lungs. The abdomen moves forward and back, and the diaphragm up and down (Figure 10). For example, singers and musicians, and writers breathe using the "abdomen" type.

Full Yoga breathing is a combination of using all three types of breathing.

Full breathing leads to movement of respiratory organs and muscles. It provides the body with maximum amounts of oxygen, stimulates immune and endocrine systems, and heals heart problems. You can do this exercise in any position - standing, sitting, lying down, or walking. Inhale slowly after expiration. At first fill the lower part of the lungs with air while pulling abdomen forward; then the middle part ribs and chest are expanded. Finally, the upper part of the lungs and scapulas are raised. At this point the abdomen

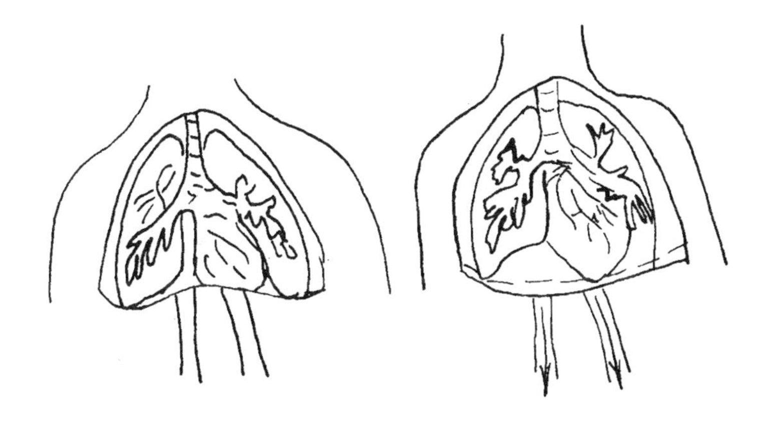

Figure 10. Full Yoga Breathing

stretches back to the spinal column. Delay expiration with a rhythm (count to eight), and start expiration slowly. Draw in the abdomen, lower ribs, chest and shoulders. The movements have to be smooth, gentle, delicate, and without pressure.

Gymnastics for Joints

Gymnastics develops joints' flexibility and prepares the body to perform more complex Yoga poses and exercises. Moreover, people may perform exercises for joints anytime during the day when sitting for a long time. It relieves tension and tiredness.

1. Sit on a chair and raise locked hands over the head. Spring on buttocks (like lifting self), and push the body forward (right and left). Work with both buttocks at the same time.

2. Sit on a chair, hug your back with the left hand and palm facing outwards from the body; touch the left knee with the right hand. Turn the torso back around the left shoulder. Stay in this position for a while, and breathe. During the breathing you may imagine that you send prana - life energy - to the kidneys (in the back, above the waist). When you exhale, imagine throwing out toxins. Change positions of your hands and repeat the exercise.

3. Sit on a chair. From the posterior hold your elbows with your hands at your back. Do not touch the torso with arms. While expiring, bend the torso to the right, then to the left. Keep your spine straight. Concentrate your consciousness on kidneys. When you exhale, you may mentally send prana to the stretched part of the body.

4. Sit on a chair. Pull hands forward and lock fingers keeping palms out. Turn your locked hands the opposite way (keep palms in).

5. Sit on a chair. Put elbows on the table and clench your fists. With pressure, lay the right palm down on the table while the left one stays in place. Change hand's position (feel your hand like spring). Do this exercise 4 - 10 times.

6. Put your elbows apart on the table, keep palms together, draw in stomach, pull in the chest, and bend your spine. Do it 10 - 15 times.

7. Sit on a chair, and put your hands on knees. Rotate shoul-

ders around one way and then the opposite way. Keep breadth as wide as possible. Do it 10 - 25 times.

8. Sit on a chair. Pull the hands and legs forward. Spread them apart, then together, then up and down. You can change the tempo.

9. Sit on a chair and put hands with locked fingers on back of the head. Exhale, push your head and neck until facing the floor. Inhale, return your head slowly to its original position. Do it 2 - 5 times. During the exercise keep your attention moving alongside the spinal column beginning from kidneys to the thyroid.

When you are doing Yoga exercises, breathe through the nose. Exhale before inhaling. In Yoga exercises, special attention is always paid to the "energetic" exhalation that helps remove toxins, wastes, and massage internal organs.

Do Yoga exercises with concentration of your attention on specific organs or places. Remember that prana around us. When you inhale, prana is transformed through energetic centers (chakras) into "Life Energy". While you use Full Yoga Breathing, at inhalation, mentally imagine how "prana (silver-blue substance) comes through the respiratory system and enters the solar plexus. At expiration, prana goes to every cell when you do " Full Yoga Breathing" exercise, or to the organ of concentration when you do Yoga pose.

Cleansing Respiration

Inhale with full yoga breath. Pause. Exhale portions of air through tightly closed lips.

Therapeutic effect. Eliminates stress and tiredness of the respiratory system.

Drawing the Abdomen in

Do this exercise without moving when exhaling. Stand with feet about two feet apart (Figure 11). Concentrate your attention on the solar plexus and the blood circulation in the veins.

Exhale, and then take a slow gentle yoga inhalation while raising both hands at same time. Make a sharp energetic "huh" - expiration through the mouth- and exhale the rest of the air. After expiration, pause in breathing and pull muscles diaphragm up to the spi-

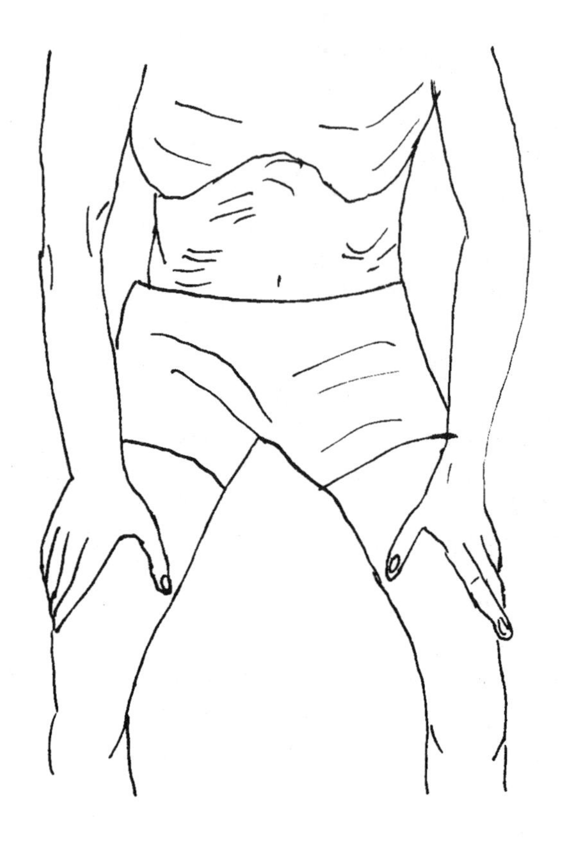

Figure 11. Drawing Abdomen In

nal column. Keep knees bent and put hands on the hips and leg joints. Make "a neck lock", or touch the throat with the chin. Stop breathing for 15 seconds (you can add one second each day until you reach your maximum). Return to the start position and begin to breathe slowly and gently.

Therapeutic effect. Stabilizes the circulation system and digestion.

Respiration Exercises

1. Keep the proportion of the inhalation and the expiration at 3:1 ratio. You can sit or stand during this exercise. No breathing halts are needed. Concentrate attention on your nose pathways. Exhale and inhale, and sharply pull out air from the lungs while drawing in your abdomen. Inhale, shove the abdomen out and exhale soundly and quickly. Inhalation occurs automatically, and it is passive. The main attention should be exhalation.

2. Inhale through the nose, then do the previous exercise, but close the left nostril with the right middle finger. Inhale and close the right nostril with a finger, and do the exercise through the left nostril.

Therapeutic effect. Develop muscles used for breathing, the diaphragm, and the lungs. It influences the nervous and digestive systems. It massages organs in the lower abdomen area.

The Lion Pose

Stand in the Diamond pose (see Figure 7). Start with the deep expiration, and then make a full yoga inhalation. Concentrate your attention on the thyroid (your throat).

1. With expiration put the tongue outside the mouth. Tense the muscles and pull fingers apart from each other.

2. Pull the tongue back, and touch the hard palate of the mouth, and push the jaws forward.

3. Push the tongue outside the mouth for a few seconds.

4. Place the tongue on the hard palate of the mouth.

5. Push the tongue out for a few seconds one more time.

Meanwhile keep your muscles tensed. Then relax the muscles.

Repeat the exercise a few more times. Keep eyes opened, and look up towards your brows (eyes should be closed during any other poses).

Therapeutic effect. Influences the respiratory and circulation systems. Helps to heal angina and speech defects.

The Mountain Pose

Stand straight, keep your feet together, and draw in the stomach. The chest is straight with hands hanging loosely alongside the body. Concentrate attention on your waist. Look straight in front of you (Figure 12). Stay in this position for 1 - 2 minutes.

Therapeutic effect. Controls muscles, teaches right position of the body.

Leg Lifting

Lie down on your back and place the hands alongside the body. Concentrate your attention on organs of the lower part of the body. While inhaling, lift both legs up to 90 degrees, then lift the lower body up helping with both hands. Fix the heels on the line with your eyes. The body should stand on the elbows, and head stays on the floor. Do not touch the chest with your chin (Figure 13). Try to breathe using stomach muscles (lower respiration).

Therapeutic effect. Improves biochemical processes in the body and memory, changes face color, and stimulates organs of the lower abdomen.

The Candle Pose

Lie down on the floor and relax all muscles (Figure 14).

1. Make a full expiration, and with a gentle inhalation, raise your legs slowly and gently making a 90 degrees angle to the body.
2. Repeat leg's lifting keeping the legs perpendicular to the floor.
3. Touch your chest with your chin. The head, neck and upper shoulders stay on the floor.
4. Breathe slowly using stomach muscles.

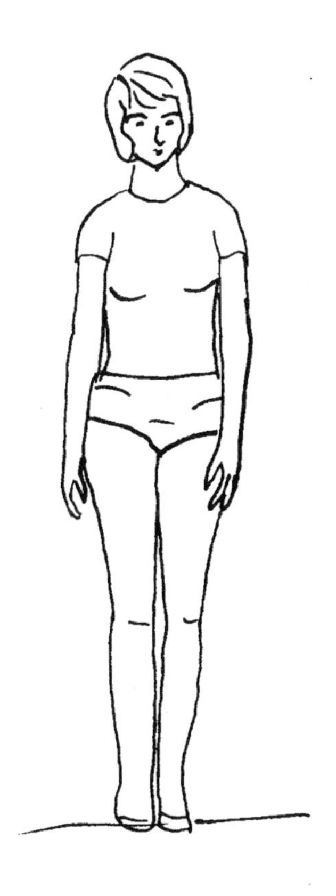

Figure 12. Mountain Pose

Figure 13. Leg Lifting

Figure 14. Candle Pose

5. Keep attention on the thyroid.

6. Begin with 30 seconds, and add five seconds every day. Later you can do this exercise 1 - 5 minutes.

7. Bend your knees and lower legs down slowly.

Therapeutic effect. Trains the vessels of the brain and rests the heart, lungs, and endocrine glands. Additional blood enters to the systems. This exercise stimulates nervous and digestive systems, and organs of the abdominal cavity.

Breathing Exercise to Strengthen Lungs

Stand in the Diamond pose. Keep the torso, shoulders and head in one line. Look straight ahead. At first do sharp breaths slowly, and then very quickly through the nose. Repeat this 15 times.

Therapeutic effect. Strengthens lungs and normalizes their work, influences the central nervous system and spinal cord, and increases energy levels.

"Huh" Breathing

1. Stand straight, keep feet apart on shoulders' wide. Take a deep breath and slowly raise arms straight over the head. Stop breathing for a few seconds, and bend the torso forward sharply while bringing the hands down. Exhale through the mouth with "huh" keeping stomach tight. Return to the initial position. Take a deep breath slowly and raise your arms. Exhale through the nose and lower the arms back.

Concentration: When you stop breathing after the inhalation, imagine that you take a bag of your troubles in your hands. With "huh" expiration you throw the bag over a high mountain, and all the troubles are gone. Your soul becomes free and calm.

2. Lie down on the floor. Slowly raise your arms and lay them down on the rug above the head. Delay breathing for a few seconds, then draw your legs quickly to the stomach bending them at the knees. Hug them with your hands, and exhale while announcing "huh" during this exercise. After a few seconds make a slow inhalation, and raise your hands over your head. Raise your legs perpendicular to the body. After a pause, exhale through the nose and put arms and legs down. Relax your body.

Fish Pose (Counter Pose)

This pose is better to do after the Candle Pose.

Sit on your ankles. Concentrate attention on the heart and solar plexus. Keep your spine straight. Place hands on knees. Helping with both hands and elbows, bend your body backwards until the head touches the floor. Exhale and bend your spine outwards from the floor while lifting the neck and chest. Try to touch the feet with the head. Touch the ankles with the hands (Figure 15). Time period for the pose lasts between 30 seconds to one minute. With inhalation, return to the beginning position. Lie down and relax.

Therapeutic effect. Stimulates abdomen organs and strengthens its muscles, fixes spinal column defects, and activates the nervous, endocrine, and circular systems.

Plough Pose

Lie down, keep legs together, and hands alongside the body with palms down. Concentrate your attention on the spine column. With expiration lift legs straight up slowly until they reach a 90 degrees angle with the floor. Bend your body and lower your legs over the head and touch the floor with the toes (Figure 16). Put out the legs as far as possible trying not to bend them at the knees. Keep the hands in the first position. It helps to stretch the spine. Stay in this pose between 30 seconds to two minutes.

Therapeutic effect. Normalizes biochemical processes. It influences glands, liver, spleen and kidneys.

Exercise to Strengthen Nervous System

Keep legs apart, shoulders' wide. Make a deep expiration. With a slow inhalation pull your hands forward with palms up. Clench your fists, bend arms at elbows, and pull them to shoulders. Quickly repeat the movements a few times. Bend the torso forward and exhale. Relax and lower the arms.

Therapeutic effect. Self-confidence.

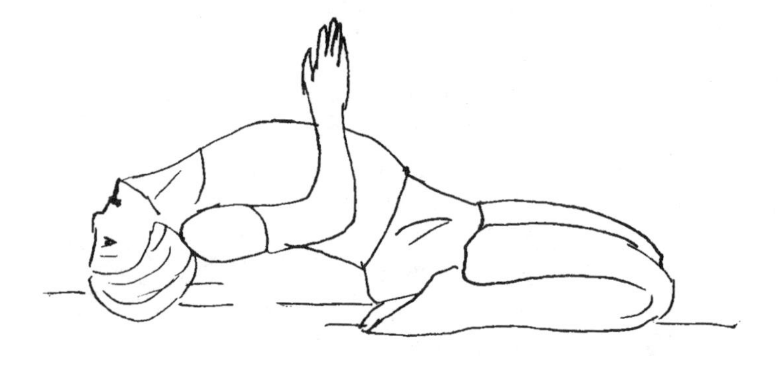

Figure 15. Fish Pose

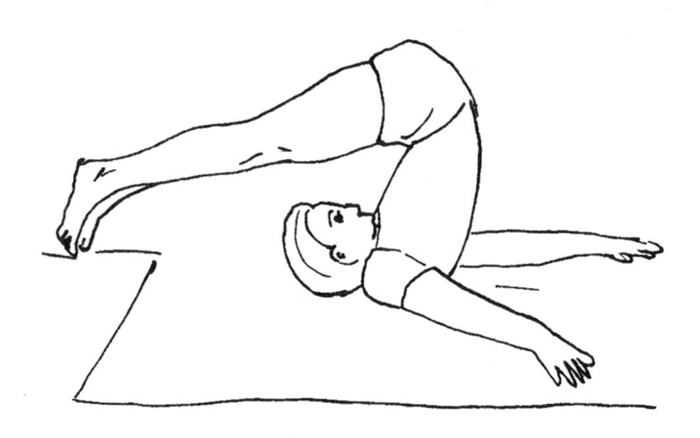

Figure 16. Plough Pose

Bending the Body Outwardly

Concentrate your attention on the lower back.

1. Stand as in the Mountain pose (see Figure 12). With a full expiration, bend the torso forward (try not to bend knees). At the end of the expiration, touch the knees with the forehead (Figure 17). Stay in this position as long as possible, and then go back making a full yoga breath. Slide hands along the legs.

Therapeutic effect. Stimulates organs of the abdomen, and makes the spinal column more flexible.

2. Lie down on the floor keeping legs together. Concentrate your attention on solar plexus. With a full yoga inhalation, raise arms over the head with the palms out. With a full yoga expiration, bend the body at the hips while moving toward the legs. Try to touch knees with forehead and toes with fingers. Try to keep knees straight. When you exhale, stop breathing for as long as possible; inhale and return to the original position.

Therapeutic effect. Affects organs of lower body and strengthens the solar plexus.

Tree Pose

Stand in the Mountain pose (see Figure 12). Bend the left leg at the knee, take left foot with both hands and place it on the right hip joint (keep bent knee on even plane with the body). Put palms together and raise the arms over the head (Figure 18). Stand for 1 - 2 minutes. Return and repeat the exercise with the right leg.

Hero Pose

Sit down on the floor keeping the feet apart. Concentrate your attention on the legs. Pull your ankles and place them alongside your thighs (heels touch hips). Spine should be straight. Place hands on knees (Figure 19). Stay in this pose for a minute. Use this pose for the training of proper breathing, concentration of attention, and meditation.

Therapeutic effect. Helps to relieve pain in the knees.

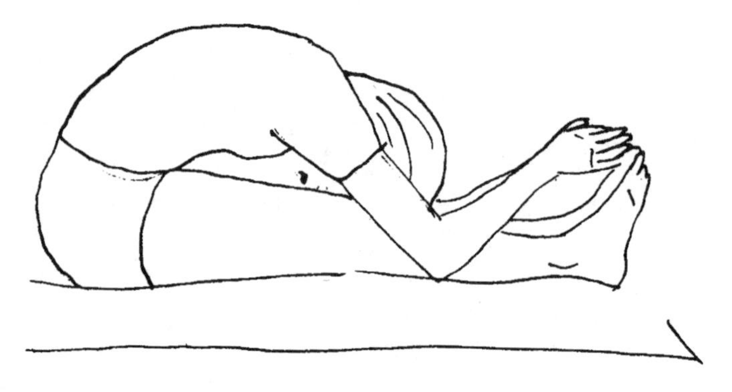

Figure 17. Bending Body Out

Figure 19. Hero Pose

Figure 18. Tree Pose

Pose to Strengthen Spinal Column

Sit down on the floor pulling the legs forward (Figure 20). Concentrate the attention on the spinal column. Bend right leg at the knee, and draw it to the chest and hold tightly. Pull right leg over left hip, and put right foot on the floor besides left hip. Put the right hand behind the spine at the waist. Put right leg under the left armpit, and place the left hand on the right leg. Stay in this position for 20 - 30 seconds. Change the position of legs symmetrically and repeat exercise.

Therapeutic effect - Treats defects of the spinal column, influences liver, spleen, and bladder.

Snake Pose

Lie face down on the floor. Concentrate your attention on the thyroid, and then on the sacrum (the lower part of the spinal column). Lay the hands with palms down in line with shoulders. With the inhalation, while pressing floor by the hands, gently lift the upper body up and bend the spine. The lower part of the body stays on the floor.

Delay breathing after inhalation. Tense the buttocks and turn the head to the left to see the right heel (the spinal column turns over too). Keep the posture for 15 - 20 seconds. Relax the buttocks. With expiration, lower your body and head.

Therapeutic effect. Stimulates the thyroid, kidneys, spleen, and organs of the reproductive system. It develops flexibility of the spinal column and relieves muscle pain.

Snake Pose (with Straight Arms)

While in the same start position as the Snake Pose, push torso up with straight arms and toes (keep legs straight). With a full yoga expiration, pull the head back and bend the spine as in the Snake Pose (Figure 21). The consciousness slides from the thyroid to the sacrum. Pause after the inhalation for 7 - 12 seconds. With expiration, return to the original position.

Therapeutic effect. Improves activity of kidneys and liver.

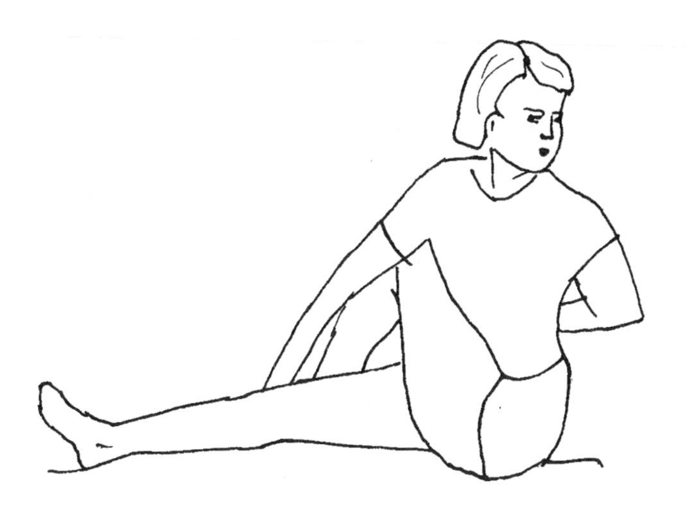

Figure 20. Pose to Strengthen Spinal Column

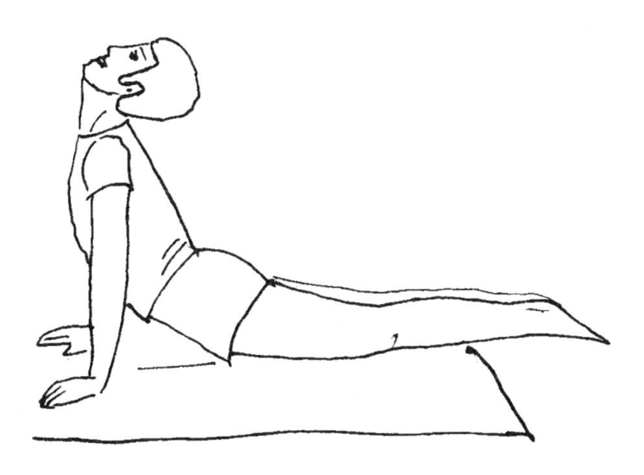

Figure 21. Snake Pose (Straight Hands)

Grasshopper Pose

Lie face down on the floor (Figure 22). Keep the attention on the spine column. Keep legs together and hands together alongside the body. Clench fists. Make a deep inhalation. Pause in breathing. Raise legs straight as high as possible helping with fists. Return to the original position. You can do the same exercise, but raise the legs separately (Figure 23).

Therapeutic effect. Stabilizes the diaphragm, heart, and circulatory system. It develops spinal flexibility, strengthens body muscles and lungs.

Exercise for Lowering Blood Pressure

Sit down on ankles. Concentrate your attention on the thyroid. Keep your body straight and hands on the knees. Make a deep inhalation. Delay breathing and when you exhale chant the mantra "Oh" (A-O-O-U).

Side Angle Pose

Stand in the Mountain Pose (see Figure 12). Concentrate attention on the lower back. Make a full yoga inhalation. While jumping, put the feet apart and raise the hands to the shoulder level on both sides with palms down. Turn the right foot 90 degrees outside and the left-about 60 degrees. Bend your right leg in the knee up to 90 degrees. With expiration, put the right palm on the right foot. Pull other hand over the head. Keep left leg straight (Figure 24). Keep the posture 20 - 40 seconds. And, then return to the beginning position. Do this exercise to the other side also.

Therapeutic effect. Reduces fat layers on the waist and hips, and lessens arthritis pain.

Star Pose

Sit down on the floor bending your legs at the knees. Join feet together. Concentrate your attention on the lower back. Lock the fingers and hold your feet. Push on your knees with elbows putting

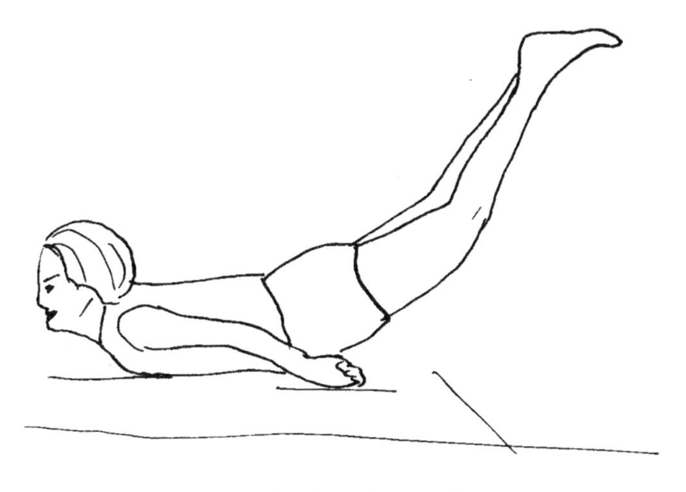

Figure 22. Grasshopper Pose

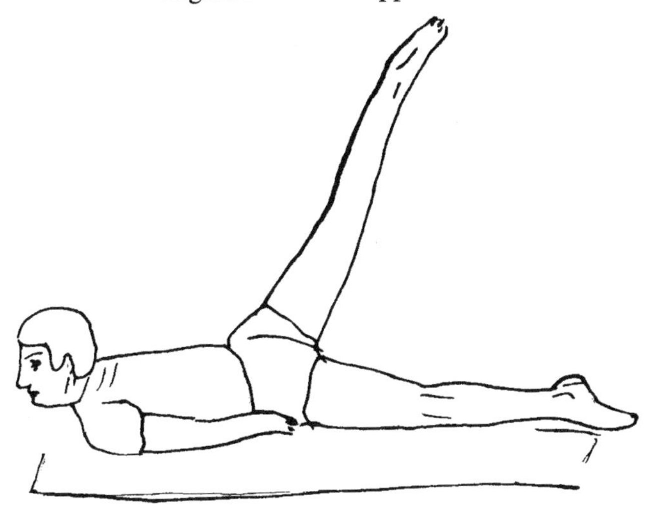

Figure 23. Grasshopper Pose (2)

Figure 24. Pose With Angle to Side

them on the floor. With a full yoga expiration, pull the body for ward and try to touch toes with your head (Figure 25). Stay in this posture between 15 to 40 seconds. With expiration, lift your body back up.

Therapeutic effect. Influences kidneys, bladder and prostate gland.

Dolphin Pose

Stand on the knees. Concentrate your attention on the thyroid. Put your head on the floor with hands and locked fingers. Lift the lower part of the body and straighten your legs. Try to stand on the head by pushing the legs up. After a few attempts return to the initial position.

Exercise to Improve Digestion

Lie flat on the floor with spine down looking up to ceiling. Put hands alongside the body, and keep feet together. Relax.

Raise your left leg as high as possible (keep the both legs straight), and bring it back. Repeat the movement with the same leg 5 - 10 times. Alternate with the other leg. Raise both legs together a few times.

Lake Pose

Lie down on the floor and relax (Figure 26).

Make a full yoga expiration and delay breathing. Draw in your stomach to the maximum. Your stomach cavity will remind you of a lake. Pause breathing as long as you can. Stand back with a slow inhalation through the nose.

Therapeutic effect. If you do this exercise correctly, problems in digestion will disappear, and functions of intestines will be improved.

Figure 25. Star Pose

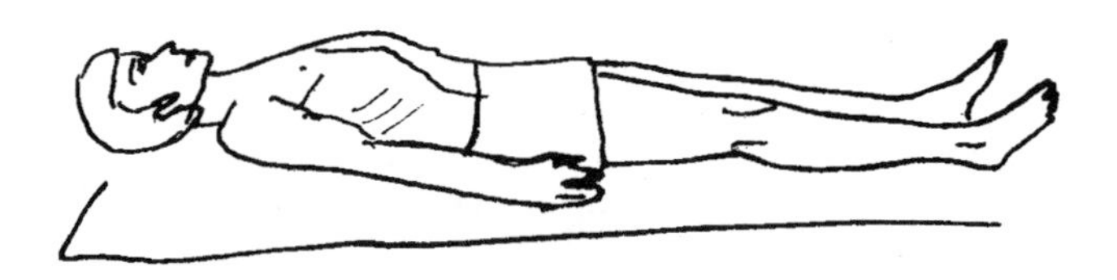

Figure 26. Lake Pose

Exercise to Strengthen Abdomen Muscles

Lie down on the floor keeping legs together. Concentrate your attention on organs of the abdomen. Spread arms and hands apart from body with palms down (Figure 27). Raise both legs 90 degrees from the floor, and lower them slowly to the right and to the left. Return to the initial position. During the exercise the entire spine stays on the floor.

Therapeutic effect. A good tonic for the abdomen.

Exercise for Stronger Liver, Spleen, and Kidneys

Sit down on the floor spreading both legs apart. Concentrate your attention on the thyroid. Bend the left leg while putting its heel under your right hip (the foot rests along right hip). With expiration, bend the torso forward. Take toes of right foot with your hand. Pause breathing for 10 - 15 seconds.

Return to the initial position. Repeat the exercise with the other leg.

Boat Pose

The left knee is bent under 90 degrees, and the right leg is straight on the floor (stands on the toes). The attention slides from thyroid to the sacrum (down the spinal column). Hands hang loosely alongside the body. With the full yoga expiration, pull the head back. Bend the spine and pull the chest forward until it touches the left knee. At this moment, the palms touch the floor. Stay in this pose for 5 - 10 seconds. With expiration, return to the initial position. Change leg's position.

Therapeutic effect. Normalizes the work of the abdomen organs.

Pushups

Lie down on the floor (face down), and keep hands alongside the body. Concentrate the attention on the solar plexus. Make a full yoga inhalation. When you delay breathing after inhalation,

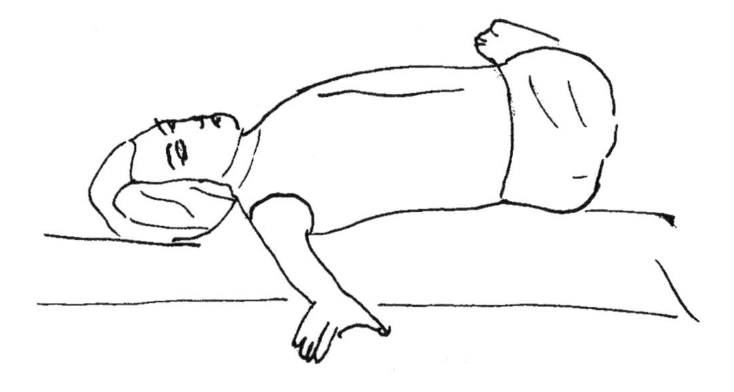

Figure 27. Exercise to Strenghten Abdominal Muscles

put palms near shoulders and push the body up and down. Keep the body straight. Repeat as many pushups as you want. Afterwards lie down on the floor and exhale through the mouth with "huh" sound while pushing the hands forward.

Therapeutic effect. Strengthens muscles of the body and normalizes respiratory system.

Zigzag Pose

Lie face down on the floor. Keep hands on the floor at chest level. Delay breathing after a full yoga inhalation and push your body up. With a full yoga exhalation, push the buttocks up and lower self on five points: knees, chest, chin, hands, and feet. Pause breathing as long as you can. Push body up and down. Inhale, and lie flat on the floor. Relax.

Therapeutic effect. Strengthens muscles of hands, legs, and the respiratory system.

Cat Pose

Concentrate your attention on the solar plexus. In the same original position as Zigzag, push up with straight arms, legs and toes. Inhale. With exhalation, push hips as high as possible (arch your body), and place feet on the ground. Lower the head down to the stomach. Draw the stomach in. Pause for 10 - 12 seconds with expiration. Relax the stomach. With inhalation, return to the original position.

Therapeutic effect. Influences organs of the abdomen.

The Exercise to Improve Flexibility of Spinal Column

Concentrate your attention on the upper spinal column. Stand on your knees. Keep the forehead on the ball of the fists (one fist on the floor and another on top of the first one). Bend neck and touch the floor with the chin (bend the ball of the fists as well). Stay in this posture for 10 - 15 seconds. Return to the start position.

Therapeutic effect. Makes the spinal column flexible; and strengthens glands of the endocrine system.

Half-Lotus Pose

Sit down on the floor. Push legs forward. Put left foot under right hip. The right heel touches the stomach. The torso, neck, and head should be in straight line. Put the hands on the knees. Look forward (Figure 28). Stay in this pose up to one minute. Push the legs forward, and repeat this exercise changing feet.

Angle Turned over the Body Pose

Stand with feet 2-feet apart (Figure 29). Concentrate your attention on the lower back. With inhalation, raise your arms to shoulder level. The right foot turns 90 degrees outward, the left one at 60 degrees; the right knee bends up 90 degrees. Exhale. At that moment turn the torso to the right. Pull left hand over the right knee to the right foot. Keep the right hand and the head up. Stay in this pose as long as possible. Inhale and return to the starting position. Repeat the exercise with the other leg.

Therapeutic effect. Influences organs of the abdominal cavity, digestive system, and develops flexibility of the spinal column.

Diamond Pose (Lying down the Floor)

Sit down in the Diamond pose (see Figure 7). Concentrate your attention on the solar plexus. Put heels apart behind your hips. Helping with elbows, lay on your back, with hands at the back of the head or neck (Figure 30). Lie down on the floor and relax, and return to the Diamond pose.

Breathing Exercises to Heal Colds and Flu

1. Sit in the Half-Lotus pose (Figure 28). inhalation takes 3/4 the length of a whole breath (expiration - 1/4). Concentrate your consciousness on the energetic center between brows (Ajna chakra). You can inhale for three seconds, and exhale for one second. Take three breaths.

2. Use the same as the previous exercise, but inhale through both nostrils, and expiration through one nostril (at first the right,

Figure 28. Half-Lotus Pose

Figure 29. Angle Pose (Turned Over Body)

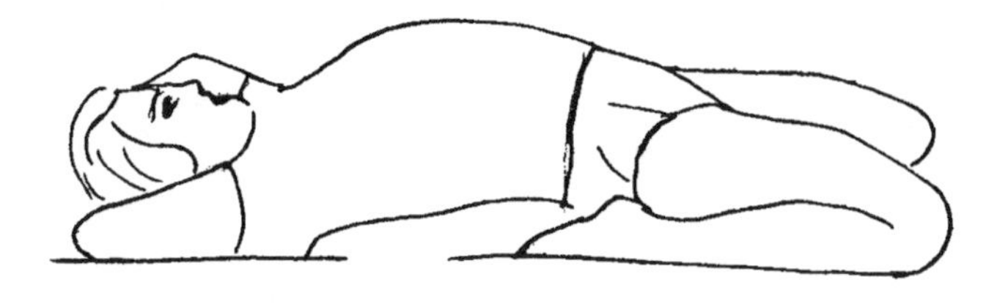

Figure 30. Diamond Pose (Lying On the Floor)

Figure 31. Triangle Pose

then left). Close the other nostril with a finger.

3. Make the Diamond pose (Figure 7). Inhale through the right nostril while regulating the intake of air with a thumb, slowly pressing on it and closing left nostril with a finger. Delay breathing after the inhalation. Press muscles of the lower body and pull them up to the spinal column. After a pause for 2 - 3 seconds, regulate expiration through the left nostril with a finger. Repeat 3 - 4 times.

Therapeutic effect. Cleanses the nasal cavity, breathing ways, lungs, and heals colds and flu. Improves the nervous and digestive systems.

Triangle Pose

Stand with feet about two feet apart. Keep hands hanging loosely alongside the body. Concentrate your attention on the spinal column. With a full yoga inhalation, raise arms with palms up to the shoulder level. Exhale. Bend torso to the right, touch the right foot with the right hand, and raise left hand vertically (Figure 31). Face the left hand at the end of the expiration. With the inhalation, return to the start position.

Repeat the exercise changing position to the left.

Therapeutic effect. Relieves constipation, improves work of the intestines, develops flexibility of the spinal column, and strengthens muscles of the chest, hands, and legs.

Triangle Pose (with Turn)

Everything is the same as the previous exercise, but, with exhalation, bend the body to the right and try to touch the left heel with fingers of the right hand (Figure 32).

The left hand is raised, all muscles are tensed, and hands are kept straight. Stay in the position 20 -30 seconds, and return to the original position. Repeat the exercise bending to the opposite side.

Breathing Exercises to Stimulate Endocrine System

1. Stand keeping the feet apart, and the hands hanging down. Concentrate the attention on the heart. With a full yoga inhalation,

Figure 32. Triangle Pose (With Turn)

Figure 33. Fisher King Pose

raise hands forward to the shoulder level, and ball fists with thumbs inside. Pause breathing and do circle movements with fists as many times as you can. Stop fists in front of chest and exhale through the mouth making "huh" sound. Open fists. After exercise, do cleansing breathing.

2. With a deep inhalation, raise arms with hands open and both palms together over the head. Concentrate your attention on the heart. Delay breathing and press palms together. Hands are straight. Keep the entire body under pressure (as you would try to fly). Keep eyes closed. You can move the torso, but keep legs and hips fixed. With a full expiration, turn palms out, and lower them to both sides of the body and do cleansing breathing.

3. Stand near a wall keeping legs together. Concentrate your attention on the heart. With a deep yoga inhalation, raise your hands to shoulders. Pause. After inhaling, raise your hands and fall against the wall. Touch the wall with the forehead and support body with fingers. Push away from the wall with fingers, and fall against the wall again. Exhale after last pushup with the "huh" sound, and push the body back. Do cleansing breathing.

4. Stand with feet apart. Keep hands on hips. Concentrate your attention on the solar plexus. Make a full yoga inhalation. Exhale and bend the body as low as possible. Pause breathing for 3 - 4 seconds after expiration. Inhale and pull the body back. Again with a full yoga exhalation, bend the torso back, and pause breathing for 3 - 4 seconds. With a full inhalation, return the body to its initial position.

With exhalation, bend the body to the left and return back when inhaling. Do the exercise to the right 2 -3 times.

5. Sit in the Diamond pose. Concentrate your attention on the heart. Make a deep yoga inhalation with pressure (stopping few times to breathe with noise). Stop breathing for 7 -14 seconds, and exhale slowly.

Therapeutic effect. Stimulates the endocrine system. Makes the body stronger and flexible, strengthens respiratory organs.

Fisher King Pose

Sit down on the floor, and keep legs straight (Figure 33). Concentrate your attention on the spinal column.

Bend the right knee and pull it inward. Put the heel under the left hip. Bend left knee and pull it over to the right hip and place the foot on the floor. Turn the body to the left so that the right armpit touches the left thigh. Hold the toes of the left foot with your right hand. Pull the left hand back behind the spine. Turn the head and the body as far as you can. Keep the chin over the left shoulder. Stay in this pose for 30 - 40 seconds. Return back and do this exercise turning the other side.

Therapeutic effect. Makes spinal column more flexible, fixes deformities and influences liver, kidneys, and pancreas.

Bow Pose

Lie face down on the floor and keep hands alongside the body (Figure 34). Concentrate your attention on the spinal column and lower back. Bend knees. Hold ankles with both hands. Arch your body by pulling your head and legs up as high as possible. You can rock your body for effects.

Therapeutic effect. Stimulates organs in abdominal cavity, and develops flexibility of the body.

Peacock Pose

Sit on your knees and ankles. Concentrate attention on the pancreas. Put forearms together, and spread knees apart. Place elbows on the pancreas (between the belly button and solar plexus), and put palms under the buttocks (with fingers facing back). Go down and touch the floor with the forehead (the buttocks pulled up). All body weight is kept on hands and forehead. Straighten your legs. Stand on three points: feet, forehead, and palms. Pull head and legs up, and hold yourself on your hands. Lower legs and head to the floor, and support your weight with the knees.

Therapeutic effect. Influences the pancreas.

Camel Pose (Partial)

Sit down on knees and heels (Figure 35). Concentrate the attention on the spinal column. Inhale and push the head back. Lift

Figure 34. Bow Pose

Figure 35. Camel Pose (Partual)

the body until hands touch the heels. Stand in this pose using muscles of the spine and the body. Exhale in 30 seconds and return to the original position.

Therapeutic effect. Good for endocrine and circulatory systems.

Stand on the Head

Concentrate your attention on the thyroid. Stand on knees and put head on the floor in a bowl made by hands locked together (Figure 36). Straighten legs, and elevate buttocks. Bend legs at knees, push the body up, and stand on the head. Raise the legs. Stand in this pose between 10 seconds to a few minutes. Bend knees and lower your legs to the floor.

Therapeutic effect. Trains vessels of the brain, activates work of the pituitary gland, hypothalamus, and other parts of the brain; influences the circulatory, nervous, and digestive systems.

Internal Massage of Organs

Begin this exercise when you can draw the stomach in and out 500 times a day and more. Concentrate your attention on the abdomen. Stand in the Fisher King Pose (see Figure 33). Tighten muscles of the stomach and push them forward. After a few seconds, press the left knee with the left hand. Bend to the left, and tighten and push muscles forward on left side of the abdomen. Pull right side muscles forward (Figure 37). Rotate muscles of the abdomen (clockwise).

Caution: Do this exercise on an empty stomach.

Therapeutic effect. Perfect massage for internal organs, improves activity of liver, kidneys, pancreas, and stomach and intestines.

Swallow Pose

Stand with feet apart and hands hanging loosely alongside the body. Concentrate your attention on the lower back. Inhale and raise your hands head over, and put hands together (Figure 38). Exhale

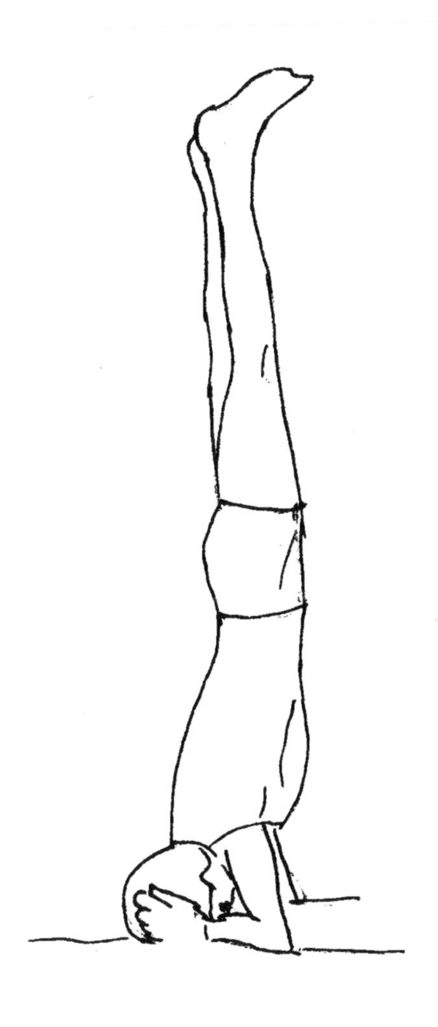

Figure 36. Stand On Head

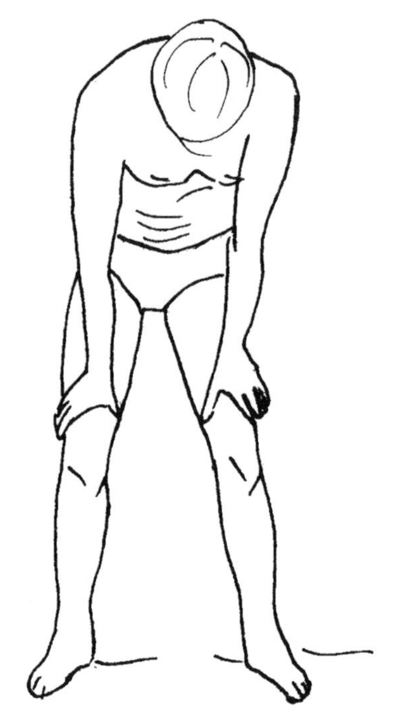

Figure 37. Internal Organs Massage

Figure 38. Swallow Pose

and turn the torso and feet to the right. Bend the right knee 90 degrees with left leg straight. Pull head back and straighten your shoul ders. Stay in this pose between10 -20 seconds. Return to the initial position.

Repeat the exercise for the other side.

Therapeutic effect. Helps remove excess fat on hips; strengthens muscles of the spine, legs, and hands.

Lotus Pose (Classic)

The "Lotus Pose" is one of the best yoga positions for breathing exercises, concentration, and meditation (Figure 39).

Sit down a rug or small pillow, and push legs forward. Bend the right knee. Take one foot by hands and place it on opposite hip so that the heel touches the lower part of the abdomen. Repeat the same procedure with the other foot. The knees should stay down on the floor. If they don't, at first, be patient. The knees will descend slowly as the meditation time lengthens. The spinal column, neck, and head are kept in a straight line. Put the palms of hands on the knees. Concentrate on your inner-self. Stay in this pose for a minute, and then push the legs forward again and rest. Repeat the exercise alternating legs.

Bending Body Forward

Stand with legs apart. Inhale. Bend the body making it parallel to the floor. Bend the spine inward and put palms on the floor. Stay in this position between 10-15 seconds. Lower the body and put head on the floor. Keep hands bent at the elbows. The feet, palms, and head are kept in straight line. Stay in this position for 30 seconds. Inhale and return to the initial position.

Therapeutic effect. Develops elasticity of the spine and stimulates the organs of the abdomen.

Wheel Pose

Stand straight, with feet apart. Concentrate your attention on the lower back. Raise your hands over your head. Slowly bend your

Figure 39. Lotus Pose

body back. Bend knees when you lower your hands to the hips. Continue to bend them until hands touch the floor. After this straighten your legs to increase the bend of the spine. The time of this exercise ranges between 20 seconds to one minute.

Therapeutic effect. Stimulates nerves of the spine, and helps relieve digestive problems.

Sofa Pose

Sit down between both heels as in The Hero Pose (Figure 19). Concentrate the attention on the solar plexus. Exhale and bend your spine back. Lie down on the floor helping with hands and elbows. Pull your hands over your head. Bend the spine and touch the floor with your head. Weave your hands together, and put them behind the head. Stand for a minute. Return to the initial position and relax.

Therapeutic effect. Activates the organs in the abdominal cavity.

Rabbit Pose

Stand on the knees. Exhale and bend the body to touch the knees with the forehead; put palms of hands on the feet (Figure 40). The legs are at an angle of 90 degrees to the knees. After 10-15 seconds, return back to the initial position when you inhaling.

The purpose of Yoga exercises is to help maintain a perfect body, and stay flexible, center self, concentrate attention, hear the inner self, be able to breathe deeply to prepare self to receive bio-energy, free of toxins. Yoga can be a part of everyday life. It will help you maintain your body and mind in perfect health without experiencing stresses and anxieties. This is the way to discovery opportunities to heal self, family members, and pets through development and uses of bio-energy.

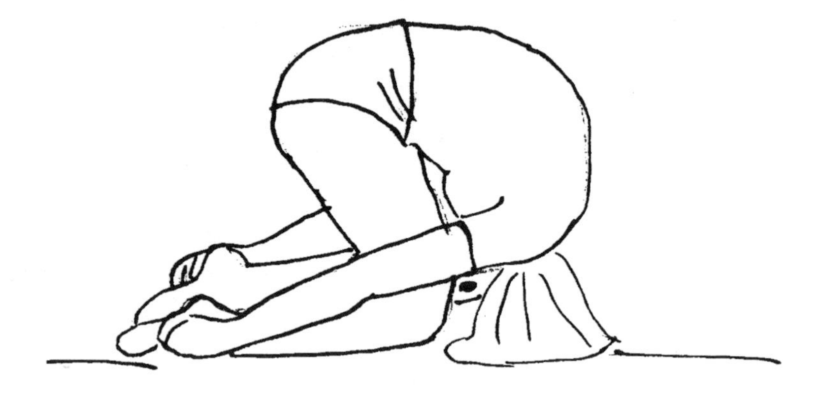

Figure 40. Rabbit Pose

Chapter Five

Development of Abilities to Feel and Identify Energy Fields

This chapter describes techniques to develop the abilities to feel and examine human fields, determine and identify own energy fields and those of others, and receive an energetic information from energy fields in forms of "signals." Steps to develop ability to heal and maintain bio-energy include development of strong and capacious memory. You will learn special exercises to improve your memory, and develop instantaneous concentration and centering as on the inner self as on mental images and energetic sensations of other people.

You will learn to feel differences in the energetic field, recognize familiar feelings, to perceive patterns of feelings and conditions, and recognize your own field. You will also learn your moving energy to control it. In addition, you will develop the ability to heal, and learn how to develop energetic pathways in your fingertips.

"Activation" of energetic pathways in fingertips is the most important step in bio-energy healing. "Activated" hand is a working, exploring, and healing hand. You will be able to perform bio-energy work with "activated" hands. "Activation" of energetic pathways means opening energetic pathways in your fingertips which already exist on fingertips. Bio-energy flows through your fingers when the pathways are activated. You will be able to send healing energy to others as well as restore it after work receiving it from the cosmos and using "activated" pathways in hands. The following special exercises can help you to activate healing energy in your hands, and practice can make you an advanced master.

"Activation" of Healing Energy in Hands

1. Put your fingers apart. Bend them as if you had a ball (Figure 41). Start to "bounce" your palms so one thumb enters the space between thumb and fingers of another hand (like horseshoe enters the space of another horseshoe). Produce the movements to achieve a feeling of energy flow between hands that feels like subtle woven threads.

Effect. Ability to open and develop pathways of bio-energy in fingertips.

2. Concentrate attention on the left hand, feel warm, weight, and sensation. Mentally move a ball of the concentrated energy from the left to the right hand throughout the shoulders transferring energy with eyes and then do this in opposite way.

Effect. Ability to feel flow of your own energy.

3. Turn one hand clockwise around another hand motionless without touching each other. Explore what you can "feel" with the hand "activated by static electricity." Pass your "activated" hand over the table, feel some sensations (character of these sensations is personal, in general - warm, "weight", and fullness). Pass empty space following after the table and feel the difference (cold, emptiness).

Effect. "Activate" energy of your hands every time you exercise with static electricity.

4. Place your hands apart about 6 inches with palms facing each other. Start to "bounce" hands bringing them close to each other and far (without touching each other). Keep moving them like if you would play catch. "Feel" your energy that is flowing between fingers of both hands.

Effect. Energetic "activation" of hands.

5. Rotate one finger of one hand around each finger of another hand without touching (Figure 42). Change the finger and follow with the same procedure. Repeat until you finish exercise with both hands. It will take about 7 -10 minutes for this exercise.

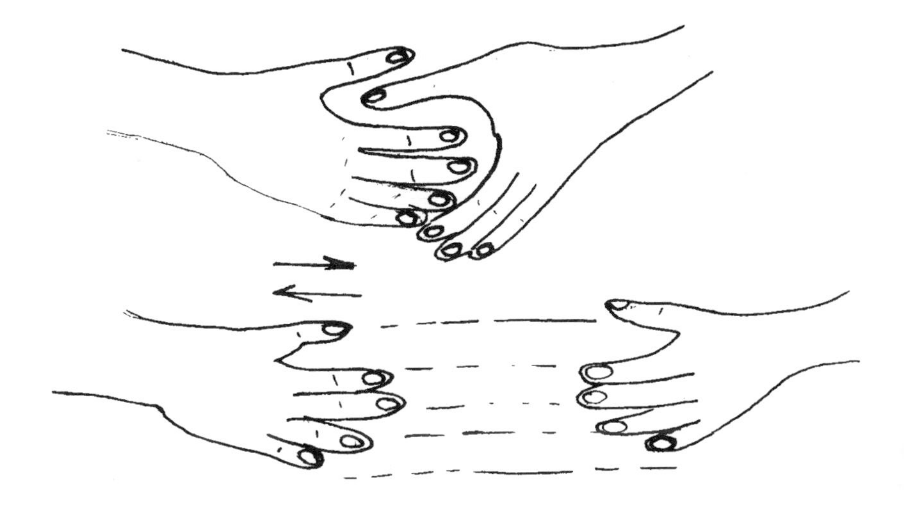

Figure 41. Exercise (1). Opening Bio-Energetic Pathways

Figure 42. Exercise (5). Opening Bio-Energetic Pathways

Effect. Practice of opening pathways in the fingertips for energy to flow, develop sensitiveness of fingers.

The next step in developing the ability to feel your own biological energetic field, and that of others and ability to heal self and others, is to learn attention and memory techniques.

Consciousness, Attention, Memory

Every individual has a different consciousness ranging between actions of recognizing self to recognizing unity with the Cosmos (superconsciousness). According ancient traditions every subtle energetic body of human field of energy has its own energy of consciousness and energetic centers (chakras) are centers of consciousness. Developing of energetic can deeper their consciousness. For example, Yogis can manipulate their consciousness, but it takes years to develop mastery. All anyone needs is to be able to concentrate attention. Attention is defined as the concentration of energy of the consciousness on one or more objects providing their bright images.

The condition of deep concentration of attention is the main factor in feeling energetic fields. Capacity of attention is also important. When you possess the ability of deep concentration of attention, you can attain the point of "Consciousness Light" (point of perception of incoming energetic information), and direct it to any place in the energetic contour of another person. The point of "Consciousness Light" controls a person's perception of the world. With its help, we are able to learn to perceive energetic information from other worlds as well.

We offer the following exercises to develop concentration, capacity of attention, and quickly switch attention:

1. Take any object like a box of matches, put it in front of you, and try to concentrate your attention on it for a minute. Think only about this object as follows: "This box has a rectangular form; it is dark blue; it has a picture on it; there are 10 matches inside; the box is made in good quality; I like it; I can use this to keep nails; it can float like a boat; and so on."

This exercise develops imagination. In the beginning other thoughts may enter your mind and interfere with your attention.

Push them away and concentrate on the object. Begin with one minute and keep adding an additional half minute each day. Do this exer cise until you feel tired. In the second month of practice you can add music (an interfering factor). Do this exercise two times a day for three months.

2. Yogis often use the following exercise to demonstrate the technique to concentrate attention. They take a few different kinds of stones, put them on a table, and observe them for three seconds. Then they describe every one of the stones in detail (color, shape, size and so on).

Usually, attention capacity is 5 - 7 objects at once. Nevertheless, you can increase it up to 9 or more objects. Your consciousness will be able to reach the highest level after this exercise. The only caution to this exercise is overstraining the brain. If you feel tired, you should stop and do the exercises later.

To increase the intensity of consciousness, you can achieve it by training of your memory (reflection of recent and previous experiences) memorizing, and recalling emotions, thoughts, and images. We have many types of memory. Conscious recollection is a blend of several types of memory:

-Word-logic-memory is a skill to hold the information with logical connections like remembering texts (left side of the brain).

-Visual memory is a skill to hold visual images. We remember visual information by the right side of the brain. Information may be remembered using images or hooks. It is easier to recall information with images because the right side of the brain is less busy, than the left (logical) side.

-Auditory memory is a skill to hold the information by hearing.

-Kinesthetic memory is the skill to recall perceived or remembered movement. We recall forgotten phone numbers, because our fingers know which buttons to push.

-Emotional memory is the skill to remember and recall certain emotions and senses. Emotional moments are remembered easier and for a longer time.

Memory is not a sense, and people are not born with memory that could be referred as good or bad. But memory is a skill that can be developed and improved.

Exercises for Developing Memory

1. Sit down in a comfortable pose, and relax your body. Read any text of with about 10 sentences and distinguish the details, images and links. With closed eyes, try to recall the text mentally. Imagine and "see" it with all its details. Break the text into 10 parts (Figure 43). For example, if you forgot the sentence from fourth part, you could:

(a) recall links from the fifth part going back and forth;

(b) recall all links returning from the last one;

(c) recall links beginning from the most well (remembered) link and going back;

(d) recall links beginning from the most remembered link to the forgotten ones. If after trying you do not recall the forgotten link, read it one more time. With time, you can increase your memory of the text up to one page.

2. Ask someone to write ten numbers in ten squares. In 10 seconds try to remember the order and nuances of the writing. Train every day. You can reduce your time to three seconds. You can use this exercise when working with any kind of texts.

3. Before bedtime, sit in a comfortable position. Try to recall events of the day in reverse order. With all the events, try to recall emotions, feelings and images. Do this exercise every day. This exercise will give you the possibility of achieving the point of "Consciousness Light" of past.

4. Using methods of self-suggestion for memory training is very productive. Before trying to remember information, relax and mentally state to self: "All that I would see, hear, and sense, I will remember easily, very steadily and for a long time; and I can recall it at any time, and everything I need. My memory has capacity of self-control. With my wish I can recall any information from my mind." After that, begin to memorize. To do this exercise often and for a long time is not difficult, and it will give you excellent results in improving memory functions.

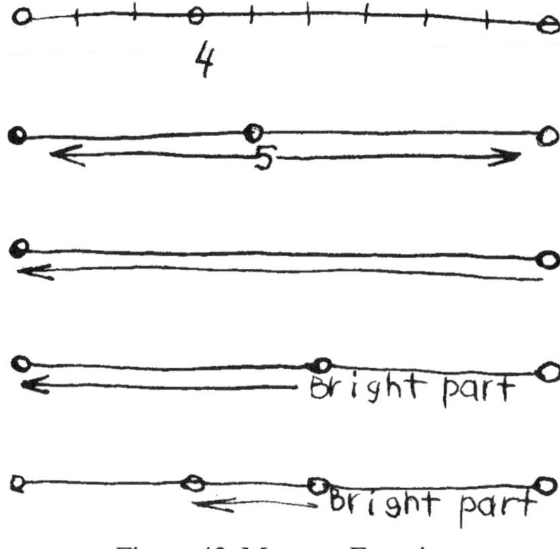

Figure 43. Memory Exercise

Concentration, Centering On the Inner Self

1. The following exercise help develop instantaneous concentration, and to maintain mental images and sensations of other people.

Take a look at something. Try to keep it in memory before your eyes for three minutes. It is preferred to do this exercise three times a day. Or, place a circle or square made of black paper on a wall and look at the shape for three minutes without blinking of your eyes.

2. The following exercise will help you to learn how to concentrate immediately on the inner self, feel your own energy, and to direct and control it.

Take a look at your left foot and "feel" your energy there (warm, fullness, weight). Slowly move this energetic "sphere" to the right foot following along legs and transferring it with your eyes to the right hand then the left hand. Finish exactly where you began (on the left foot) to avoid an imbalance of your own energy.

3. Repeat meditative yoga positions The Lotus Pose, The Half - Lotus, and breathing exercises (Chapter Four).

Exercise to Relax and Accumulate Energy

Lie down, relax all muscles, mentally "turn off " (feeling of absence) toes, feet, legs, then, fingers, hands, arms, and rest of the body. There is nothing left around you, only your consciousness continues to work. Imagine that energy comes to fill you through the pathways on the fingertips flowing to the shoulders and entering the solar plexus. You may meditate slightly, or think during this exercise: "There is instant and constant flow of vital energy "prana" entering my energetic bodies and chakras. Prana submits to my consciousness. My consciousness controls flow of "prana." I can direct, modulate, accumulate, transfer, and use vital energy. I want to heal. I have this ability. I can do it." In about 8 minutes "turn on" all your extremities gradually, and shake your hands and legs slightly.

You have learned how to develop perfect memory, breathe properly, center on inner self (meditative yoga poses), concentrate attention, increase your energy level, accumulate energy, and protect yourself from negative information on energetic level. Now you must learn how to feel energy fields and heal people with your energy.

Practice to Feel Energy Fields

1. Take anything made of cast iron or heavy aluminum. Explore it with your "activated" (energetically charged) hands without touching. What do you feel? Yes, cold. Try to feel the change in "feeling" as you move your hand away. Recognize the difference, and remember differences in sensations of objects.

2. Place a few small objects in front of you (glass, cloth, paper, wood, plastic, or metal). Pass your "activated" hand over them separately at 1-2 inches distance while trying to recognize and fix your "feelings" of the different objects in your memory. Keep doing the exercise for a week. After one week of this exercise, try to recognize objects made of the same materials with closed eyes by passing your "energized" hand over them. Try to determine their densities.

3. Repeating the exercises for developing better memory is very useful:

(a) Look at any small object for one minute. Try to see all

details, peculiarities, defects.

(b) Before going to bed recall your day with all the details, events, feelings, and nuances. Recall the same information in reverse order.

The exercises develop memorizing details that you must have when you assess human energy fields in order to remember energetic signals, energy conditions, recognizing patterns and feelings.

4. Try to determine the polarity of magnets. Remember feelings and signals of north and south poles. It leads to advanced feelings.

5. Try to determine signals of objects of different shapes. Try to differentiate and remember signals of the shapes. Try to find a certain shape with closed eyes. Try to feel the signal of a human hand. Keep all sensations in memory (your data bank). You can do the exercises when you have a free minute as often as possible to achieve automatism and mastery. Mastery of this ability demands more practice through repetition.

6. Try to determine the field of an electrical cord. Remember its characteristics.

Determination of an Energy Field

1. Determine your own energetic field. It is very important to know the "feelings" of your own field, and you will not make mistakes when assessing others. For example, you can do this by filling six glasses with water. Keep your hand that possesses opened pathways over the three glasses for five minutes (other three glasses should be uncharged). After that, wash your hands with cold water to remove any negative information. Feel your own field and the difference you will feel with "empty encountering space" comparing the glasses of water. You can ask other people to "charge" the other three glasses in order to learn to feel the difference of biofields of other people. Every person has a unique and personal field. You have to train your ability to determine your own field and of others.

2. Try to determine a human energetic field by passing your "activated" hands over shoulders of another person without touching. Try to feel energy fields at some distance. Try to feel energy

fields on pets by passing the hand over the whole body without touching. To become a master of healing, perform this assessment at a distance of 8 -10 feet. Surprisingly, you will feel sensations and power. Advanced masters "feel" and determine bio-energy fields at any distance.

Receiving the Energetic Signals

Receiving energetic signals while working with bio-energetic fields is to receive energetic information from diseased or painful organs, or locations in the body. Healthy organs or parts of organism do not signal, or transfer energetic information. When assessing, energetic information (signal), it comes on the fingertips (opened energetic pathways) of the "activated" (energized) working hand.

Signals can come from any matter - organic or inorganic. Intensity of the signals depends on many reasons, such as: kind of substance, condition, degree of pain or illness. Organic signals are stronger and more precise. Living organisms send signals with strength indicating the degree of disease in organs or places in the body. The more an organ is diseased or painful, a received signal is stronger. If there is pain in any place in the body you are working on, you would feel strong and precise signals with your hands. Signals are like heat, cold, energetic pumping and others. Types of signals, their nature, depends on individuality of a healer.

Chapter Six

Assessment of Human Energy Fields

Begin to assess the energy fields of other people after practicing the exercises of feeling your own energy. You probably will want to try it to help and heal others without touching the body.

When you obtain the "feeling" in your hands, you feel the opening of pathways in your fingertips after the exercises. Start to try out bio-energetic ability with relatives, pets, or any objects or clothes.

To think about your will to help, or to heal, is important. Ask yourself why you want to help. You must understand your answer. When healers are strongly motivated to help and heal, they achieve terrific results. Healers while working on energetic levels, have to be focused and motivated to help others attain their maximum state of well-being. Healers become involved in occurrences of projection, identification, determination, transfer, and counter transfer, and should be psychologically prepared to perform the responsibilities.

However, do not become emotionally involved in acts of energy healing. Personal interaction is dangerous. Do not open yourself to the same problem as the person you are trying to heal. You should to perform the following procedures to defense your energy system from entering negative energetic information, and to prevent becoming sick or vulnerable to the same illness or pain.

Before any assessment or healing, place your hands in a "Yoga Lock" or defensive block from negative information (Figure 44). Join fingertips of one hand with the other hand keeping the right

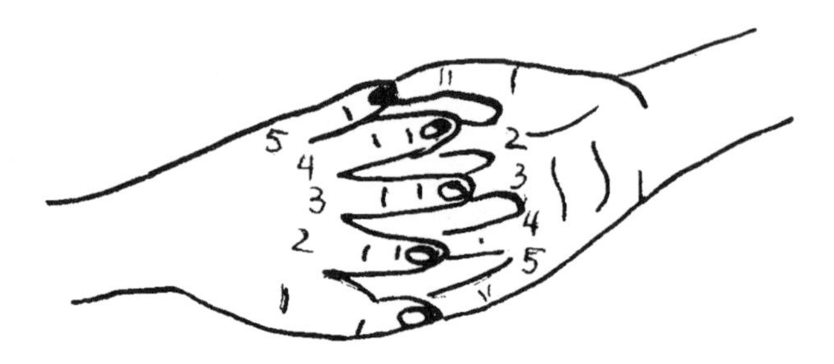

Figure 44. Defensive Yoga Lock

palm facing the body and the left palm facing in the opposite direction. Mentally tell yourself: "My illnesses would not come to you, and your illnesses would not come to me". It is very important to do this procedure before working to heal on the energetic level, and to avoid influences of negative information generated by ill organs or illnesses. Also, during the act of assessment or healing, shake your hands (3, 6, 9 times) from time to time. After work, wash your hands thoroughly with cold water. By protecting yourself thus, you will remove negative information of other energy fields.

Let's briefly summarize what must be done before beginning the assessment or healing:

1. Increase or accumulate your energy level by receiving prana energy, especially if physically or mentally tired.

2. Center the inner self, and consciously direct attention inwards, including relaxation of the body, concentration of conscious-

ness, full yoga breathing, feeling the equilibrium, and your energy flow.

3. Prepare yourself on the psychological level for the process. Concentrate on the healee and on the healing. Make the "Yoga Lock." Feel self-confidence in your knowledge and mastery, love, kindness, and willingness to help the healee.

4. "Activate" energy of your "working hand," the one that writes. On the energetic level, the working hand is stronger than the other hand. When you develop opening of pathways on the fingertips, you will feel which hand is a working hand. Do the assessment with that hand.

5. Make general assessment of the healee's energy field.

General Assessment of Healee's Energy Field

Pass "activated" hand from the head down to the feet beginning from the front side, from the back, and both sides at a distance of 4 - 7 inches from the body surface (Figure 45). Every time the palm goes perpendicular to the floor, because if the hand move by making another angle to the floor, your energy will accumulate in the feet. Place your "working" hand, with fingers apart, over the head. Move the hand down towards the floor, and finish your work by moving the hand parallel the floor.

Assessment from all four sides determines types of signals in healee's energy system. When you examine the body, concentrate attention on the signals. If you feel a pain signal, a tingling or a shot in your fingers, you should stop and repeat the procedure more thoroughly. A pain signal of different intensity is an index of an abnormality of an organ. The strongest signals are received of acute disorders, malignant tumors (coldness, breaking). If you feel a slight "emptiness" with a cutting feeling in the field of the healee, it was trauma. When receiving a pain signal, throw it away at once by shaking hands.

Through practice and creative work you will discover many various feelings. After work dispose of excess energy by "flapping" hands all over the healee's body without touching it.

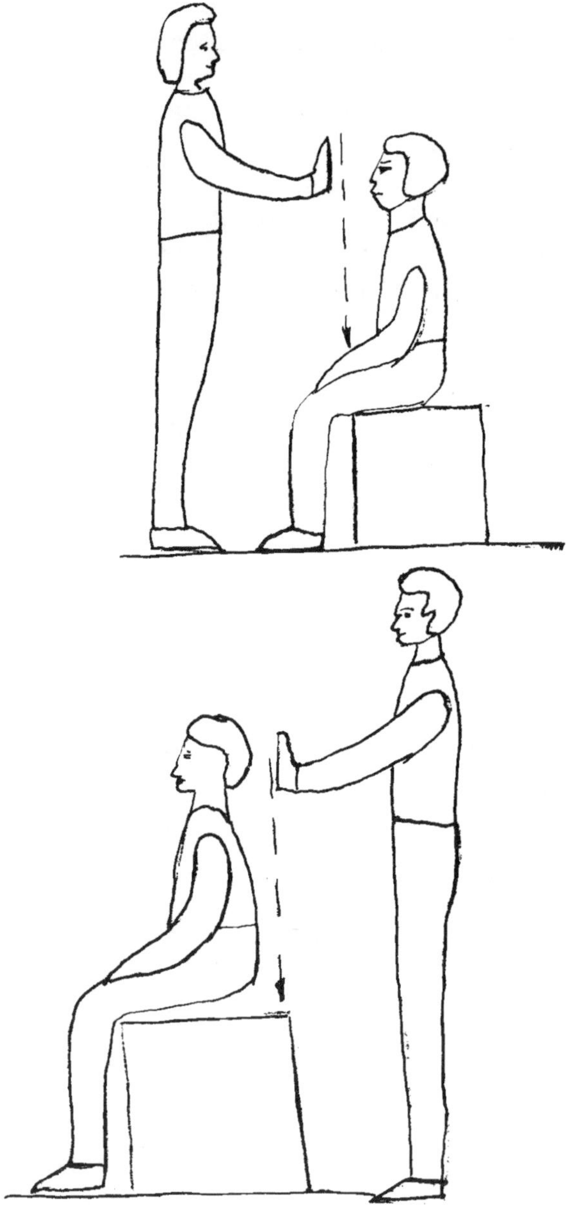

Figure 45. Assessment From Front And Back

Photograph and Image Assessment of Healee

You can perform the assessment of human energetic conditions (and physical as well) at a close distance, also with photograph or image of a person. Assessment using photos is one of many mysteries in parapsychology.

Photos carry information about a person for many years, but changes with age of the person. When assessing a person by a photo, made about twenty years ago, you will recognize current information. As a result, you can obtain exact information about the condition of a person at any time. There is no scientific proof how the information about physical condition of person exists on the photo. Photos of a dead person do not have signals (it produces feeling of unusual coldness), but an experienced healer can "read" the kind of illness or reason for death.

To prepare yourself to assess the physical condition of a person in a photo, close your eyes and mentally tell yourself: "When I take a look at the photo, I can feel this person easily, calmly, effortlessly with energy of my hands." Open your eyes, take a full yoga inhalation, and, then, using the "activated" vibrating hand pass it over the photo beginning from the head down to feet (even if there are no legs shown). This creates the person's karmic body. Feelings and signals are all the same when diagnosed at a close distance with the healee. After working with the photo, shake and thoroughly wash your hands.

If you are given a detailed description of the person (height, weight, characteristic details of the figure, face and so on), you can close your eyes and mentally imagine this person (the energetic phantom of the image). You can almost visualize this person right here. Slowly begin the assessment as in the case of the photo.

Here is another method to assess by an image. Sit down and place your hands on your knees. The person in front of you must mentally imagine the healee you are going to examine (it is a person who knows the healee). You should be relaxed and in a meditative position. Let your energy flow into the person that imagines the healee. In two minutes, details of a newly received image of the healee will appear in your consciousness. Relax your working (writing) hand and send the energy through your fingertips on the phantom that you see. Draw it out from another person, and picture the phantom in front of you. You practically feel the phantom near you. Just start the assessment.

Detailed Assessment

When you are "energetic", center on the inner self, and psychologically prepare to perform assessment of the energy field of the healee. "Activate" your working hand and begin the detailed assessment from the head down to the feet. First, we assess in front of the body.

We will describe practices and experience of extrasensory people.

The techniques are not a substitute for professional medical examinations or treatments. If you are ill, you should visit a medical doctor.

Head

Pass your "activated" working hand over the head. If you feel:

(a) a dispersed signal, it means the healee has spasms of vessels;

(b) a signal on the forehead (like a sphere on the energy field), it means low blood pressure;

(c) the same signal but on the back of the head, it means high blood pressure; and a pulsating signal on the back of the head means temporary high blood pressure; and

(d) a signal on the temples means trauma or inflammation of facial nerves.

Eyes

Examine the eyes with one fingertip. If you feel that eyes signal unequally, the difference means that the sight of one eye is better than that of the other. If one eye signals more intensively than the other, it is worse.

While working with the healee and you discover a signal, always examine that place or organ with one fingertip of the activated hand to get greater understanding of the signal's nature. After that you should remove the signal by clearing it with both palms (move one palm to the other, and shake hands and fingers) to eliminate negative information from the healee's field.

Ears

A mild signal in the ear can indicate that the illness is chronic, and a strong signal means that the illness is acute at this time.

Nose

A signal in the nose and nasal cavity means an inflammation in the place that signals.

Teeth

You can examine the teeth, also. If there is no tooth in the place, or it has been treated, you will feel a signal. Explore with the fingertip. Also, check the gums. The signal would indicate an inflammation.

Larynx

When you examine larynx, be aware of signals from thyroid and tonsils. They signal differently. The thyroid signal acts as if it is far away.

Shoulders

A signal from shoulders means that the person has layers of salts.

Heart

The heart is not healthy if a signal pumps (energetically) into the hand.

Breast

If the breast signals by dots, glandular inflammation (check by the fingertip) could be the cause. If breasts and uterus signal the same way, a woman has a menstrual period. If they signal with different intensity, she is a pregnant.

Stomach

If the healee has stomach problems, and a precise signal (small spot), it means the person has an ulcer. An uncertain signal means that the person has gastritis. Check acidity of the digestive system with the finger. Pass your finger along the esophagus (digestive tract). Low or high acidity signals appear as burning sensations.

Organs of the Abdomen

If you receive the same signal from the liver and spleen, it could mean hepatitis. And if the signal is in the liver, it means a reaction to food.

Spleen signals occur when there is blood illness in the organism. Pancreas signals occur when there is diabetes. That signal repeats in the urinary bladder.

Appendix signal by a signal in form of stripe, if operated, and by energy shaped signal, if inflamed. If pain is acute, the received signal is strong, and in a case of chronic condition of appendix, the signal is blunt.

When you examine small intestines and receive the signal (like sphere on the field and coldness), colitis is present.

If the whole kidney signals, it could be nephritis. If there is a dot signal, it could be sand or stones in the kidneys. If you receive a dot signal from ureter or urinary bladders, sand or stones are present also. If kidneys signal as a whole, it means an inflammation. If the urinary bladder signals as a whole, it could be cystitis.

The Assessment from the Back

Lungs

When we examine the lungs, and they signal as a whole, it could be pneumonia. If they signal by spots, these spots could be "dark spots"- hearths on lungs.

The signals that show pneumonia and tuberculosis are almost the same, and they are determined and differentiated by practice.

Vertebral Column

The condition of the vertebral column is very important for general health. Assess the column carefully, because nerves go through every vertebra and they "connect" to every organ. You should check every nerve. If there is a compressed nerve in the vertebra, and it signals, the organ is affected, too.

Elbows

If the signal comes from elbows, it means muscular pain.

Spine

If the signal flows from the left scapula, the person has neuralgia.

Lower Abdomen

Lower back pain and osteoporosis signal in the place. Uterine tubes and uterus signals come from the back. If they signal as a whole, there is an inflammation (determine by both hands). Tumor signals as foreign matter.

Legs

The signal coming from legs means arthritis, varicose veins, or trauma of the knee. Signals from the toes mean dermatitis and eczema on the feet.

Needless energy could be accumulated in the healee during the as sessment. We need to dispose it (Figure 46). For this purpose, place hands over the head making a roof, pass down to the feet, and finish on the floor. Shake and wash your hands with a cold water.

When I assess the person's bio-energetic field, and I feel a large clot in the energy field as a signal. It suggests that negative energetic information is in the place of the field. My main task is to lead it out of the field by certain techniques (you will learn about in the next chapters). When I feel that a signal does not occur any-more, it means that negative energetic information was led out, and the person feels better.

Figure 46. Disposal Energy Accumulated During Assessment

Chapter Seven

Healing by Bio-Energy

You must not try the method of healing with bio-energy on persons who have thrombosis, appendicitis, abscesses, or bacterial infections.

Take off all metal accessories. Invite the healee to do the same, because energy should go into the healee and not be distracted by metal. Do not let the healee place feet and hands together (this way you will receive weak energy from the person).

You can be seated when you heal organs of the abdomen by your energy, but the healee should stand in front of you.

Do not heal several illnesses at one time. Other illnesses are treated no less than in two months after the first course of healing.

You can perform four acts of healing on the healee once a day in four days, then healee can take a break for a week. Afterwards, you can do four acts more in four days. In the future you can perform more when needed.

Duration of the act of healing is approximately 15 minutes (no more than 25 minutes). At the end of 15 minutes, only two conclusions arise: (a) the natural limit of healing has occurred; or (b) effect of healing continues (so proceed up to 25 minutes beginning with "activation" of your working hand again).

Make any movements in clockwise direction when using energetic healing.

The self-confidence and confidence that you must possess

are very important in a process of helping and healing. Mentally suggest to yourself: "I want, I can, I have the abilities to feel on the energetic level and to heal by energy."

Mind controls bio-energy or accumulated Prana-energy (life power) from the cosmos, and healing with this energy can affect electrical waves of the brain, and elicit a relaxation response (alpha and theta brain-wave patterns). The ability of influencing and healing with human bio-energy can be acquired, learned, felt and directed by mind while it in the alpha and the theta state.

There are two methods of healing:

1. Eliminating the pain from a place where it is felt; and
2. Trying to find, determine, and influence the origin of the illness.

In order to heal you use the working "activated" hand for removing weak energy of the healee, or sending your energy. Use the other hand - indicator - for screening the examined place to help to recognize or direct the signal more easily. In healing any illness by energy, before giving the energy to the healee, remove "feeling" of the signal: Make spiral movements with the working hand over the place of signal leading weak energy outward from the healee (Figure 47). Thus, you will remove negative energetic information from the healee's bio-energy system.

Before the healing act you have to:

- make a reception of cosmic energy -prana;
- center yourself to the inner self, breathe by yoga, relax, and concentrate on flow of energy;
- psychologically prepare your mind for the healing act and think positively,
- make yoga "lock of defense" (lock hands with one facing you and the other facing the opposite way, and each finger should touch each finger of the opposite hand);
- while keeping the yoga lock, tell yourself mentally: "My illnesses will not come to you, and your illnesses will not come to me, OM...";
- "activate" your fingertips on the working hand by opening energetic pathways, and let the energy flow through these pathways

Figure 47. Removing Weak Energy

when you need it;

- perform assessment of healee's energy field from four sides, and recognize places with energetic imbalance marked with signals.

When you discovered energetic signals in specific places of healee's energy field and recognized them, you should perform bio-energy healing using your "activated" working and "screen" hands without touching. Follow with the healing techniques.

Healing Techniques

Low Blood Pressure

Check the blood pressure with the working hand. Pass the hand over the forehead and back of the head. Feel where the signal comes from.

If you feel a signal of low blood pressure, you perform spiral clockwise movements with the working hand beginning from the sacrum (lower vertebral column) to the back of the head without involving a static screen by another hand at this time (Figure 48). Keep working at the distance of 2 -3 inches without touching. Do this procedure a few times to normalize the blood pressure. Secure your healing to avoid your energy to blow out the healee.

When you are not experienced enough, to perform the energetic act of healing with mastery, we suggest you perform the healing to visualize the process, and mentally imagine the organ to be healed, or process it in order to heal. So imagine that your energy flow (that follows the vertebral column of the healee's body) can direct blood flowing to the brain. At this time, send blood to the head with spiral and circular movements of your energy (by hand).

To Lower High Blood Pressure

In case of high blood pressure, let the healee stand with the back to the north.

Place your screen hand (indicator of signal) at a distance of two inches from the forehead. Place your working hand on the back

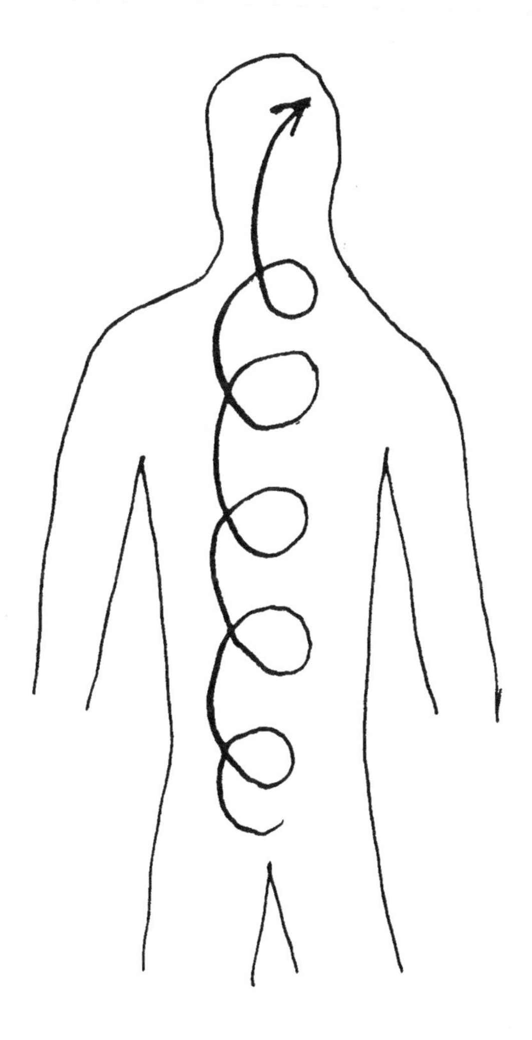

Figure 48. Spiral Movements to Normalize Low Blood Pressure

of the head (two inches from the head). Send your energy to the back of the healee's brain, mentally imagining that the flow of en ergy sends the blood down the vertebral column to the sacrum; and make spiral movements about eight inches in diameter (clockwise) with the working hand from the head down to the sacrum. You can move the screen hand as you go.

Concentrate your attention on the hypothalamus. Perform the movements 15 - 20 times to normalize blood pressure. Secure the healing on the person, and shake your hands three times. Wash your hands after each act of healing, in order to remove negative energetic information.

Release a Headache

The healee should stand (or sit) with the back to the north. Determine where the signal (epicenter of the pain) is located in the healee's head. Place your "static screen" hand on the opposite side of the head at the distance of 2 -3 inches from the head (facing palm to the head). If a headache occurs, for example in the forehead, place the screen hand behind the head, and place your working hand over the place of the signal (2 -3 inches from the head). Take off the signal with spiral, clockwise movements (with increasing diameters of rotation) while moving the hand away from the head with the working hand. At the end of the process, shake your hand.

In a case of migraine, the pain can move to other places of the head while being influenced by the healing energy. If the pain moves, put the screen behind the initial place and root out the signal from the other place with spiral hand movements (increasing cycles in diameter and moving the hand outwards). Draw out the pain signal from both spots. Secure healing (for males - from the right to the left, females-in the opposite way). Shake your hands three times afterwards.

If you close your eyes after you determined the pain location, you will see dark spots (energetic pain spots) on the cloudy background. You should remove negative information from the healee's energy field, and fill it up with your healing energy. When you stop seeing dark spots and even colored background, then stop your work.

To refresh the healee's head, just spin your working hand around making clockwise movements over the head.

If the head is light, dispose the weak energy. Place your hands to form a roof over the head. Pass both hands down to the floor and finish your movements on the floor.

If the healee feels pain in the temples, place hands over the temples. Put the screening hand over one temple and the working hand over another. With your active hand make spiral (clockwise and outward) movements and lead the pain (signal) out of the temple.

In a case of spasms of vessels (numbness of a leg or a hand) , put the screen with the hand behind the signal's location, and drive the energy of your active hand into the signal's place. With the active hand make wave-like flaps of the palm. The wave-like flaps direct the energy into the signal's place. Do the movements until the pain is gone. You can feel the strength of the signal with the screening hand. Follow your hand's spiral movements along the spinal column down the leg by leading the weak energy out of the leg of the healee. Shake your hands and wash them in cold water.

Eye Problems

If the healee has eyesight problems (weak eyes, blurred vision, swollen, bloodshot, burning eyes, itchy, or watery eyes), begin the healing by sitting the healee down and put their hands on knees.

1. Place your screening hand in the middle and on the back of the healee's head doing one eye at the time. With the "activated"(working) hand make spiral movements (direct clockwise, towards the eye, and decrease cycles in diameter of rotation as the hand approaches the eye). Thus, you give your energy to the weak eye. Every time you perform the act of healing keep the screening hand and start the work with your active hand 2 - 3 inches away from the healee.

2. With the active hand approaching the eye, put the screening hand over the temple, and make rotational spiral (clockwise, towards the head, and decreasing rotations as approaching the eye).

3. Put the screening hand in front of the eye (no touching), and work making spiral movements with your active hand near the back of the head, and, later, near the temples. Send your energy inward to the head toward the eye. Move your hand clockwise around the

head while performing healing of eyes.

4. Secure your healing by flapping of both hands towards the head from both sides of the head (or bouncing movements of hands with fingers placed apart).

Ear Problems

You can heal ears, when noise or feeling of shooting is present. Place screening hand - an indicator - over the healthy ear. Put your working hand with fingers apart over the weak ear. Start flapping movements with the active hand towards the ear. Send your energy to quicken the process of healing. Secure your healing. Flap both hands towards the ears from both sides a few times.

Nose

When the person has a running or bleeding nose, use the method of healing using bio-energy. Place a screening hand behind the head. Keep the fingers of the active hand apart and start moving them over the nose (as if playing on piano). Start making spiral movements leading the signal with energy out of the nose. Shake the active hand every time to dispose of weak energy. Keep your active hand (with fingers apart) over the nose to warm it up (by energy). Secure your healing by flapping both hands from both sides of the head. You can stop bleeding by flapping both hands over the nose.

Toothache

You can stop a toothache with spiral movements. Place the screening hand near the back of the head (on the opposite side of a pain signal's place), and work with energetic "activated" hand. Rotate with the active hand (with fingers' flexed) around the place of pain. At first the healee could feel an increase of the pain, but in a matter of minutes the pain would be gone. In a case of an abscess use the same method, but without using screen by hand.

Cold, Flu

In a case of flu or cold keep working with the head and throat.

Put the screening hand behind the head and lead weak energy away from the face with the active hand (making spiral movements).

It is very helpful after an energetic act to influence also the acupressure points:

- the healee should sit or lie down, and relaxing the body;
- put your fingertip on the acupressure point, slightly push on the skin, and make a rotation by the fingertip (keep this fingertip contacting the point at all times);
- time of the session ranges from half a minute to five minutes.

The process of acupressure influence includes the following points in a case of flu or cold (Figure 49). Two points that are located on the forehead near the ends of the brows, another two points are located under pupils (on bones). The next two points are located near nostrils (between cheeks and the nose), And, in a case of running nose, the acupressure points are located under the corners of the lips. Influence a pair of the points at once (in a pulse rhythm - about 60 clockwise movements a minute).

Throat

In a case of a sore throat, lost voice, or pain in the throat, put the screening hand at the back of the head (of 2 -3 inches), and make a rotation (clockwise) by an active hand with fingers flexed around the sternum (located on the throat) in two to three minutes. Rotate the hand over the point located one inch down from the sternum. Put the screening hand over the upper spine, and perform spiral outward movements with the active hand.

Shoulders (Inflamed Nerves, Calcium Deposits)

Place the active hand near the side of pain. Start drawing the pain's signal out of the body with spiral (clockwise) movements of both hands. Secure the healing by flapping of both hands over the place of healing.

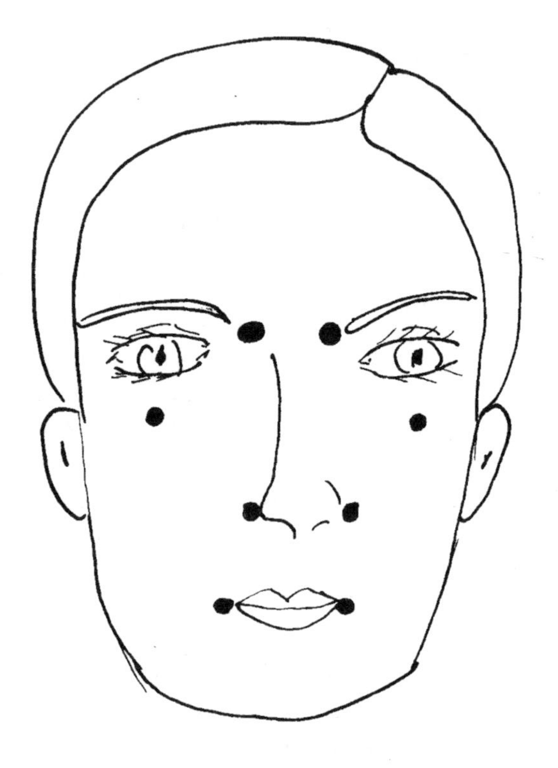

Figure 49. Acupressure Points

Put a magnet on the hand or shoulder of the healee (put the screening hand at the opposite side), and revolve the active hand over the magnet; secure the healing with slow flapping movements of both hands. Later, lead the magnet alongside the spinal column with the active hand (from north to south).

Cough

Influence the acupressure point located on the sternum (on the bone) for a half a minute. Put the screening hand with the palm towards the upper part of the spine.With the active hand draw out weak energy from the healee's upper chest moving hands in spirals.

Rotate the active hand over the upper chest giving the energy to the healee. Secure your healing, and shake the hands.

Facial Nerves

Place your screening hand near the temple, and influence the other temple by rotating the active hand (clockwise) for 10 minutes. After the process wipe the palms, and shake the hands.

Nervous Illnesses, Insomnia, Uneven Speech

Put the screening hand in front of the jaws of the healee. Rotate the active hand near the vertebral column moving the hand down the column, and repeat the same movements going up. Put the screen hand in the back of the head. Rotate the active hand in front of the jaws.

Stroke

Put the screening hand near the healee's fingers (then toes), and rotate with the active hand over the place on the head located over the ear that contains the part that accounts for its control over movements. Put the screening hand over the ear and rotate with the active hand over arm (then leg) moving it down to the fingers and toes.

Bad Blood Circulation

Rotate the active hand along the blood vessels along legs and arms.

Acne

Soak two magnets in water or keep water in a magnetic cup. Use magnetic water to wash face or wipe it with a cotton ball once a day.

Starting work over the liver by spiral, outward movements with the active hand in order to remove negative energy. You can keep the screening hand moving over the spinal column, and revolve (clockwise) with the active hand around the root chakra - Muladhara (Figure 1).

Osteoarthritis, Spondylitis (Arthritic Spine), Bursitis (Calcified Deposits)

Use spiral movements to draw out the signal of negative energy at the place of a signal. Rotate the active hand (clockwise) near the vertebral column going up and down. Or, rotate the hand near the place of the signal.

Thyroid Problems

Feel the signal. Take several steps away from the body and stop at distance where you can still feel the signal. This time the screening hand plays the role of the working hand. With the screening hand draw your energy to the thyroid with spiral move ments (clockwise). Wipe off the hands with each other (taking off the energetic signal of the problem).

Back Pain

Put the indicator hand (the screening hand) near the stomach, and circulate the energy inside the lower back with the active hand (starting with cycles of large diameter, and decreasing in diameter as the hand approaching the body, finishing with small diameter) (Figure 50). Draw the signal of weak energy outside the body.

Asthma

Influence acupressure points located in the middle of the wrist, between a thumb and fingers, four points on the throat, two points near nostrils (between the cheeks and a nose), and on the thumb and fingers (at the root of a nail). Influence these points in the order that described previously.

Put the screening hand over the place on the upper spine (at a distance) and, revolve (clockwise) the active hand around the sternum for 3 - 4 minutes. Draw the signal out, and wipe off the hand.

When asthma turns worse, add movements as if you bounced a ball. Such movements let you warm the person's chest with energy. Rotate and bounce the active hand over the chest of the healee, and go around the healee and do the same procedure from the back (the screening hand is on the stomach).

Lungs (Inflammation)

Put the screening hand over the chest. With the active hand, revolve near the back giving energy to the healee. Make bouncing movements in order to warm up the healee with your energy. Continue doing this until the signal is gone.

In order to heal tuberculosis, keep the screening hand over the chest. Draw the weak energy out of the body (by outward spiral movements), and give energy by revolving the active hand near the chest.

Plugged Duct (Breastfeeding-Related Problems)

Revolve the active hand reducing the diameter of spiral movements to the width of one fingertip. Put the finger near the place from which the signal (like a dot) is coming, and draw the signal out with the fingertip.

Or, you can draw the signal out of the breast by spiral movements (clockwise) using the working hand. Send energy by

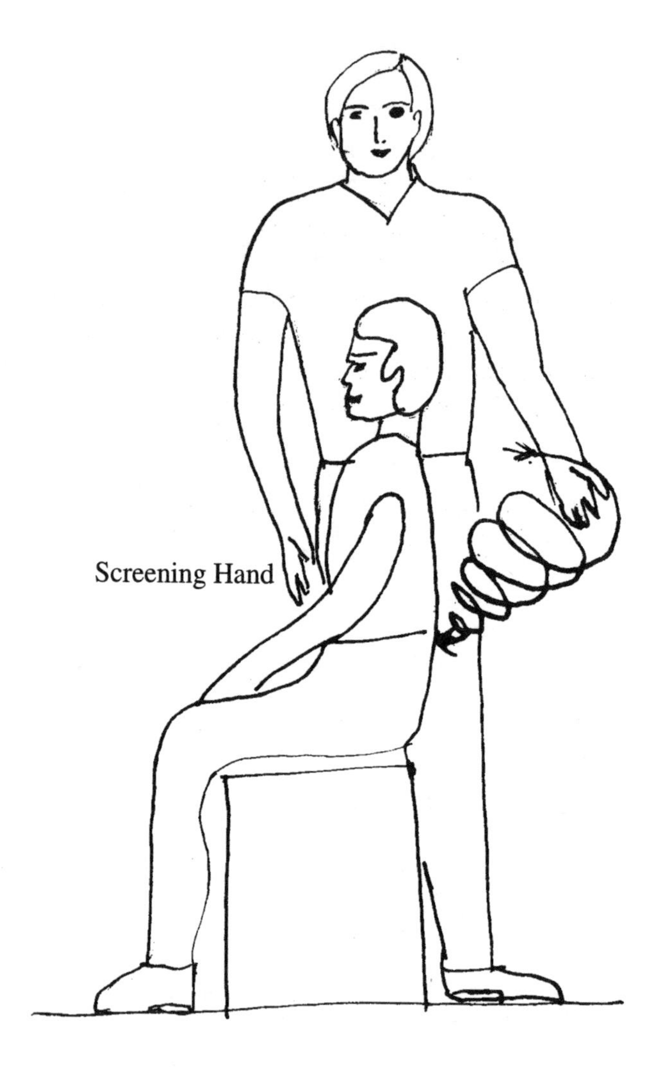

Figure 50. Donating Energy When Relieving Backache

bouncing movements of the active hand towards the breast. The amount of milk could be increased as a result of this healing act.

Heart

When you work with the heart, never use your screening hand. Use the method of drawing the signal out of the body. Slowly make spiral movements following the heart rhythm outwards. Draw out the weak energy. Wipe the signal off the palm. Revolve the hand and wipe off the signal again. You can work on tachycardia (increased heart rhythm), and post-infarction condition.

In a case of neuralgia, you can take the signal off the left scapula by the contact method (placing the active hand on the left scapula). Remove the hand and wipe the signal out. Repeat this process over again until discomfort is gone; no later than 20 minutes.

Charging Water by Bio-Energy

Energized water is used for relaxation, energetic stabilization, and for drawing stones and sand out of the kidneys and liver. Put distilled water in a jug. While looking at red cloth, start sending energy towards the water by flapping both hands from both sides and top of the jar. Keep looking at the red cloth and send energy for three minutes.

Drink one glass of this water in one hour (one sip in about every ten minutes).

Liver Conditions

The process of eliminating signals of pain coming from the liver is unusually quick. The liver reacts very well in response to the energetic hand. But illnesses of liver cannot be healed as effectively. The person must go to the doctor and take the proper medicines as well. In a case of hepatitis, the healer can work on the healee for one month.

Put the screening hand over the liver near the back, and revolve the active hand in the front of the liver giving it energy. Next, put the screening hand on the back of the spleen, and continue re volving the active hand over the liver.

Find the vertebra responsible for the liver. Put the finger of one hand on the liver and the finger of another on the vertebra on the back. Find the correct position by moving the fingers around the place until you receive the strong signal of energetic unity. Revolve the active hand over this vertebra while keeping the screening hand over the liver and, then, spleen.

Ulcer, Gastritis, Colitis

Ulcer heals in one or two weeks, but pain can be relieved at once. Determine the kind of ulcer. Place the screening hand near the ulcer (signal's place), and make revolving movements with the active hand over the spinal column. If you feel a burning sensation in the hand, then the ulcer is due to a nervous condition. If you receive a signal from the front of the body while moving the active hand over the stomach, the ulcer is gastric.

For healing a nervous ulcer, you need to calm it down. Put the screening hand near the ulcer in front of the body, and revolve the active hand along the spinal column (from the back of the body) moving up and down for five minutes. Place the screening hand near the back and make spiral movements with the active hand over the ulcer in order to draw weak energy (a signal) out the body. Begin with wide spiral movements and reduce gradually while moving the hand away. Finish the act of healing by giving the energy with "bouncing" movements over the ulcer for about twenty minutes.

To heal the gastric ulcer we need to work with the stomach. In order to regulate the acidity of the stomach, revolve the active hand over the spinal column up shoulder level. Repeat the procedure used to heal the nervous ulcer.

To heal gastritis, make spiral movements over the stomach and digestive duct. Wipe the signal off the hand as you go.

The process to heal the colitis (nervous origin) is quick and effective. Put the screening hand over the stomach. Try to determine the signal that you feel by the screening hand while moving the active hand along the spinal column. If you feel the signal, it is nervous colitis. Put the screening hand over the lower back. Work near the stomach by revolving working hand, and wipe the signal off the hand often (or shake the hand).

Pancreas Problems (Diabetes, Hypoglycemia, Pancreatitis)

When the person is ill with the pancreatic illnesses, we can see visible deterioration of sight and open wounds on the body. When you work with the healee with energy, the wounds could close in two days. Put the screening hand at the back of the body, and send your energy to the healee's pancreas by revolving the active hand over it for twenty minutes. Wipe the signal off the hand, and check the screening (indicator) hand if any signal is left. Lead the signal with the working hand along the blood vessels to the legs and hands. Revolve the working (active) hand over the liver and spleen. After the process, work with the eyes and wounds by revolving the active hand and leading any received signal from the wounds. Finish the act of healing by slowly flapping both hands over the wounds to fasten the healing by energy.

It is better to heal illnesses and organs that are located in the abdomen when the healer sits on a chair, and the healee stands in front.

Women's Illnesses (Illnesses of Reproductive Organs)

In order to heal a dysfunction and inflammation of the ovaries, you need to perform the act of energetic healing every day in an intensive way until illness is gone. Put the screening hand near the lower back (in the middle) and revolve the active hand over both ovaries for at least twenty minutes giving them energy.

Healing the uterine tubes is a very slow process (lasts for three months or more). Put the screening hand at the beginning of the uterine tube (lower body), and revolve the active hand over the end of the uterine tube (lower abdomen).

It is possible to draw weak energy out of the signal place and heal ovarian cysts or polyps with spiral (very small diameter) outward movements. Perform the act every day about one month. Draw weak energy out only, and do not send in any energy.

Impotence

Put the screening hand over the lower back without touching. Revolve the active hand moving up spinal column, and then move the hand down as many times as up. Put the screening hand over the lower back again, and revolve the active hand over the testicles, spirally moving the hand to the solar plexus. Repeat the movements for 10 - 15 minutes every day.

Inflammation of Prostate Gland

Do the healing with doctor's treatment at the same time. Put the screening hand near the back. Give the energy to the weak organ with wide revolving movements by working hand (for one month).

Kidneys (Nephritis)

Put the screening hand near the back, and send energy with the revolving active hand intensively over the kidney.

Gall Bladder

Put the screening hand in front of the gall bladder, and use spiral (clockwise) movements leading the active hand down from the back. Revolve the hand over the gall bladder without touching. Change position of the screening hand by placing it over the lower back. Give the energy from the front of the body (with clockwise spiral movements of the active hand).

Legs and Joints

You can heal by drawing weak energy (signal of pain) out of joints with spiral movements of the active hand outwards from both sides of the joints. In a case of sudden dislocation the joint of the leg, give the energy by revolving the active hand over the pain place while keeping the screening hand near the back.

Overworked Hands (Computer, Piano)

Give the energy by very slow "bouncing" movements of the active hand.

Hemorrhoids

Make the spiral movements from a place of the signal up to the intestines to draw the weak energy out in about 7 minutes. The pain will disappear at once.

Insomnia

Put the screening hand over the forehead. And make spiral movements going down by the spinal column on the back. Then, move the hand up with as many movements as you can.

Relieving the Weakness

Accumulate the prana-energy in the healee, the process was mentioned previously. Or give the energy by flapping both hands over the healee's head.

Eczema

You can heal the eczema in two weeks. You can "charge" by your energy the medicine cream, used for this illness. "Activate" energy of your hand, and send the energy to the cream, while looking at a red cloth. Do this for ten minutes. The person needs to use this cream twice a day.

Find the epicenter of the pain. Put the screening hand over the place of pain without touching. Determine the place of the signal by moving the active hand spirally along the spinal column. Stop when you feel the signal. Give the energy to the place of the signal on the spinal column (by revolving the active hand). Draw the energy out of the healee's place of pain using spiral movements. Make spiral movements over the spinal column. Work on the affected places of the skin the same way healing. After the procedure, wash your hands for two minutes.

Breast Appearance

In order to better the breast appearance you can revolve (circle) the active hand around each breast for 15 minutes a day.

Healing by Energy at a Long Distance

Healing by energy at large distances is possible and an effective process. To perform healing at a distance, healers have to be learned in all methods of healing using energetic influence and suggestion, or successfully practiced methods of controlling inner and outer energies (can use telepathy, ability to receive and send information at a distance).

The method of healing by energy at long distance is on a hologram (mental image) of the person to be healed. The healer needs to draw the image of that person clearly in their mind (mental picture), and put in front of self. It is surprising, but the healer can use this image (even not in full size, or with a larger organ to be healed, if needed). The healer performs exactly the same techniques as if healing the person.

You can try method of distant healing if you have already developed strong memory, you can concentrate your consciousness, fill yourself with the prana (cosmic) energy, control the flow of your energy, and have a positive state of mind.

Distant healing belongs to Integrative Medicine of the future. I often perform assessment and healing at a distance, which became my favorite method of healing. The distance method has invaluable advantages. When we heal a person in face, we feel in front of us equally energetic systems where energetic imbalance occurs temporarily. Effectiveness of our energy influence at close distances can be even less than when healing at a distance because of interfering of energy fields. At a distance, we increase our energetic influence greatly, because we mentally put the image of the person in the space and no more than eight inches in height and perform healing using the same techniques as at close distance. Our mind effectively controls bio-energy at any distance.

Distant healing (or absent) is an advanced form of bio-energy healing. When you master in this method, you will be able to relieve headache, any pain, and high blood pressure to yourself or your relatives in a few minutes. And it does not matter how far the healee is. You can try this on your pets helping to restore their health. They will be thankful. It really works on bio-energy systems.

Healing by Energy Using Photographs

Few methods of healing with energy, of a pictured person, exist today. Here is one of them.

Sit down on a chair. Receive prana energy from the cosmos. Put the photo on the table. Relax your body. Send your energy to your fingertips. Using three fingers (thumb, point, and middle) make circular movements and send (clockwise) the energy to the photo towards the place of pain. After every circled pass, make vibrations with the point finger in order to secure the healing (three times). Keep going for 2 - 3 minutes.

Before you start, mentally imagine the sick organ or part of the body, and make a mental statement: "My energy strengthens this organ and heals it." Also, it is important to foresee the conclusions and be absolutely positive in effectiveness of this type healing.

After the process of healing, shake your hands and charge your body with prana-energy again.

"Energetic" Stress Relief

When you are in stressful condition, take your photograph of your youth, when you was healthy. Sit in a chair. Place the photograph before your eyes. You can listen calm and nice music during this act. Relax.

Observe the photo for a few minutes until you will be able to recall pleasurable and happy moments from today to that age one moment after another. When in recalling you came to your age on the photo, close your face with palms and make throwing negative energy away your eyes and face for a few times. Thereafter, direct your hands to the photograph and perceive the energetic information taking it as cast from the photo and placing it on yourself and telling mentally: "I withdraw health, strength, positive energy, and self-confidence from that time." Your energetic and mental balance is restored now. You feel calm and self-confident.

Chapter Eight

Bio-Energetic Method in Everyday Use

People possess with bio-energy. When specially trained ability to use their bio-energetic abilities, people can direct bio-energy to their health and well-being. It is better to control bio-energy and be able to maintain health preventing illnesses and emotional discomfort. You can easily manage your physical, psychic and energetic health using your bio-energy and bio-energetic methods. There is an opening of new understanding of outer world and your innerself, and ability to control it consciously and "energetically."

Possessing developed perceptions of bio-energy fields, you possess powerful inner strength and high self-esteem. You have extraordinary perception and intuition now. You feel compassion and participation to others, and also high sense of your significance to others. You are able to help self and others to maintain health and inner peace. You can heal illnesses and discomfort with bio-energy. You carry "energetic" understanding of world, and teach others about abilities of bio-energy and mind.

Besides health, you will be able manage "energetically" your food, cars, homes, clothing, furniture, and workplace. You will be able to control anything with your bio-energy. You will "energetically" manage emotional situations or events.

Energizing Food

Our health and energy depend on our diets. Our consciousness influences diet, and consciousness is affected by the diet.

Diet and consciousness interact constantly in many ways, and the understanding of the interaction promotes health. Mental state, and the body, can be affected by absence of vitamins or minerals, or presence of toxins and other chemicals; also unsteadiness in the intake and assimilation of nutrients (carbohydrates, proteins, and fats).

The person in the household that selects, prepares, and serves the food is responsible for the maintenance health. If you are that person, try not to turn the delicate art and science of cooking natural food with life-giving qualities to the opening of cans and microwaving frozen food that could gradually weaken your family. Fresh fruits and vegetables, just picked from a garden contain energy in their nature and give us vital energy. However, in one or two days they become low in energy. Nowadays we live in cities and have fewer possibilities to eat very fresh produce. Thus, our food lack vital energy.

Kitchen must be a holy place in the house in which plant life could be started to serve the creating and sustaining of human consciousness. Food preparation is the connection between the worlds of plants and humans and the last point of that connection is the creation of the consciousness. It is important that individual's intelligence and intuition lead to complete understanding the role of cooking process in developing of consciousness.

While we live on the physical level, the science of cooking affects the whole human being: its physiology, health, mental and emotional outlook, energy, and consciousness. As an art of cooking, food preparation involves too many creative variables: selection of ingredients, conditions under which produce was grown, cookware, cooking temperature, and even feelings and temperament of a person who cooks it.. Rely on your intuition and experience of cooking. Do not worry about forgotten ingredients or substitute to another vegetable. The person cannot prepare healthy energetic meal, if in a bad mood or under stress. Enjoy your cooking which is rewarding.

Anybody who fixes dinner at home has a dream that everybody who would eat would enjoy it. Delicious, healthy, and appetizing food depends on the energy and mood of the cook. If you cook your own food, then repeat the following procedures for better effects of your looking and excellent health.

Accumulate prana-energy in the solar plexus with raised hands at the place where you prepare your food. Mentally suggest the formula: "When I fix the food, I will automatically fulfill it with energy. My food is delicious, healthy, easy digestable, and energetically strong."

Stand at the counter where you prepare your food. Using familiar wide spiral (clockwise) movements (from 3 to 5 times) by the "activated" hand, dispose negative information. Fix your food and enjoy. Refill with prana-energy if you need it.

Using Bio-energetic Method in Everyday Life

Bio-energetic ability is one of the most important qualities which humans possess. This ability is accessible for people with an open heart, who are kind and sympathetic, and ready to help their loved ones. People who would open their minds, hearts, and souls to others, can develop an amazing ability to heal and help themselves and others.

The ability to assess and heal can be yours in everyday life, not the privilege for the "chosen". The abilities can help you live better.

With your bio-energy you can control energy fields of anything either organic or not. One aspect of using bio-energetic ability is the removal of negative energetic information from any object in your home and environment. Negative energy checks can be done for clothing, furniture, especially beds, and all objects in your home, your car, and workplace. Children and pets are very sensitive to negative energy at home. Even adults can sometimes feel discomfort at home, or in their cars.

We suggest you to provide the systematic "clean up" of negative energy that can be around you using the following technique. "Activate" your hands, feel your energy in the hands, and approach any object at home. If you feel an energetic signal (usually -

heaviness), negative energy is present on the chosen object. Dispel the negative energy from the object with spiral clockwise move ments of your "activated" energetic hand outwards from the object.

Or, if you wish to cleanse the whole room energetically, you can stand in the center of the room and begin the procedure from the left corner. Start making wide rotational movements (always clockwise), turning your body around as you go, and stopping at the initial position. Make numerous spiral movements from outwards and down while you turn around and accumulate an imagined clot of a negative energy in the center below the self. After completing the process, lead it outside with spiral movements three times. When you clean your bed from negative energy, revolve your "active" hand moving the hand along it, and shake the hand in order to remove negative energy.

Why should we dispose of negative energy? Over a period of time, negative energetic information accumulates on any object like dust because it exists in our world. Negative energy can accumulate on our clothing as well. Our moods may depend on the energy level on our clothing, and if it possesses negative energy, it can affect our feelings, because our clothes are the nearest to us things. I often check the presence of it on my clothing that I wear, and if it signals negativity, I dispose of it.

Our clothes carry information about our energetic fields (it can be positive or negative). Carrying of information about people has the effect of a photograph which keep information for a long time. Positive energetic information signals are light and easy. If the information is negative, it can accumulate and be stored on the clothing(it signals by heaviness, discomfort). Of course, washing and dry cleaning remove dirty spots; however, it can remove negative energy to some extent. To remove it thoroughly you can use the bioenergetic method. After "cleansing" your clothes with bio-energy, you will be more comfortable and free; your physical body would feel healthy.

Eventually you will feel comfortable using "activated" energetic hands to assess and balance bio-energy. After you mastered in techniques of attention without concentration, deep relaxation (meditation), unfocus eyes, and yoga breathing, you will find progressively easier perceive bio-energetic fields around people and objects. You will feel the shape, texture and strength of bio-energetic fields. With regular practice you will be able to assess people and objects simply by looking at them.

There is one example of use of bio-energetic method in determination of negative energy by seeing bio-energetic fields. When automatic bread makers became fashionable, we decided to buy one. We tried to decide which one to purchase. I checked "energetically" every bread maker, and discovered a dark energetic spot on one. We bought that bread maker to see if something was wrong with it, and to prove that the method was correct. At home we put in the necessary ingredients, turned on the machine, and left it overnight following the instructions. In the morning, we found only raw bread dough (it was kneaded, but was not baked). We clearly saw the defectiveness of the machine. We went back, and changed it for an "energetically clear" one, which still works perfectly to our delight. As you can see the energetic method can help determine the workability or defectiveness of products you purchase.

One category of products which can be checked "energetically", and, maybe, the most important one is our cars. Very often they can be affected by negative energy. If we feel nervousness and irritable without reason inside the car, it definitely shows the presence of negative energy. You can check it regularly (with "activated" hand, or by "seeing" the energy field).

Once I visited a dealership in order to find a good used car. The dealer offered one to me. I checked it by my method and told him that the car had problems with the engine and related parts. The dealer was surprised but agreed. Once again, the method proved to be true.

Bio-Energetic Method and Emotional Situations

When you communicate with people, sometimes you might feel that some individual imposes negative energy upon you due talking loudly. Put the mental image of a glass cylinder around you. If after conversation you feel stressed, or deprived of energy, negative information may be left on you. We recommend you to dispose of it immediately after the person is gone. You can do movements by hands as shaking off dust from clothes (remove it beginning from head, arms, and body).

Regularly use bio-energetic defense (with energetic cylinders) against negative information described in Chapter Two. However, if after conversation you feel yourself "emptied", low energetic, and impaired, probably, met energetic vampire. If you met unprepared, and you were "open energetically", you could use another helpful ancient method. Look into the person's eyes (face expression is not important), and send the energetic flow of blue color (you can visualize it at first) into his or her eyes, and mentally let the person cool down. You can continue talking or doing something else, nevertheless, do not lose this "eye connection" for a while. You will feel better result immediately.

When you will learn all techniques in this book, you will be able to control and diminish any emotional situations, stresses or nervous breakdowns or anticipations. Do not forget to charge yourself with cosmos energy after any work on bio-energetic level.

We can not totally separate ourselves from everything that can cause negative emotions, swings of moods, stresses, and general weakness. These are the part of the real world. Nevertheless, we can enjoy amazing and wonderful aspects of our lives helping selves with bio-energy. And, with our positive spirits, which are the keys to find all the happiness and understanding philosophy of life, we will bring tranquility to our lives. Also, happiness is the main positive aspect in our lives. There is always a bright side to all the events in our lives, and with positive analysis, you will able to understand that. Moreover, happy people always bring joy to others. Presenting the happiness to others means to charge them with clear spirit, and positive energy. If we all would be able do this, then we can keep our minds, bodies, homes, and our common home - Earth - in pureness.

Bibliography

Alters, Sandra. *Biology. Understanding Life*. St. Louis, Missouri: Mosby-Year Book Inc., 1996.

Blavatsky, Elena. *Practical Secret Teaching*. Riga, Latvia: Rota, 1991.

Capra, Fritjof. *The Tao of Physics*. Boston: Shambhala Publications, Inc., 1991.

Chopra, Deepak. *Quantum Healing*. New York: Bantam Books, 1990.

Cousins, Norman. *Head First*. New York: Penguin Books USA Inc., 1989

Dale, Cyndi. *New Chakra Healing*. St. Paul, MN: Llewellyn Publications, 1996

Davis, Martha; Robbins Eshelman, Elizabeth; McKay, Matthew. *The Relaxation & Stress Reduction Workbook*, four. ed. Oakland, CA: New Harbinger Publications, Inc., 1998

Hutchison, Michael. *Mega Brain*. New York: Ballantine Books, 1991.

Ignatenko, Albert. *How to Become the Phenomenon.* Moscow, Russia: Impulse, 1992.

Ivanov, Y.M. *Yoga and Health.* Moscow, Russia: MMSP, 1991.

Kent, Howard. *Day by Day Yoga.* New York: Hamlyn, 1974.

Krieger, Dolores. *The Therapeutic Touch.* New York: Fireside of Simon & Schuster, 1979.

Krieger, Dolores. *Accepting Your Power to Heal.* Santa Fe, New Mexico: Bear & Company, 1993.

Leadbeater, C. W. *Le Plan Astral.* S. Petersburg, Russia: Bogushevsky Publishing, 1908.

Leadbeater, C. W. *Mental Plan.* S. Petersburg, Russia: Publishing Labor, 1912.

Mark, Vernon H. and Mark, Jeffrey P. *Brain Power.* Boston: Houghton Mifflin Company, 1989.

Mikulin, Alexander. *Active Longevity.* Moscow, USSR: Sport, 1977.

Rogers, Sherry A. *Tired or Toxic.* Syracuse, NY: Prestige Publishing, 1990.

Thibodeau, Gary A. and Patton, Kevin T. *Structure and Function of the Body*, ten. ed. St. Louis, Missouri: Mosby, 1997.